GREAT WESTERN LOCOMOTIVE DESIGN

GREAT WESTERN LOCOMOTIVE DESIGN

A Critical Appreciation

The Rev John C. Gibson, AKC

DAVID & CHARLES
Newton Abbot London North Pomfret (Vt)

British Library Cataloguing in Publication Data

Gibson, John C.
Great Western locomotive design.
1. Great Western Railway—History
2. Locomotives—England—History—
20th century
I. Title
625.2'61'0942 TJ603.4.G72G73

ISBN 0-7153-8606-9

Photoset by ABM Typographics Limited, Hull
and printed in Great Britain
by Redwood Burn Ltd, Trowbridge
for David & Charles (Publishers) Limited
Brunel House Newton Abbot Devon

Published in the United States of America
by David & Charles Inc
North Pomfret Vermont 05053 USA

Contents

Introduction

Any author who sets out to chronicle Great Western locomotive matters faces a daunting task in whatever way he tackles the subject. There have already been factual accounts but it seemed that there could be more in the way of analytical comment and in this book I have tried to emphasise, with enthusiasm, the many excellencies in Swindon design over a period of 100 years, and the way in which under both Gooch and Churchward GWR locomotive design was many years ahead of that on other railways. On the other hand, no one and no organisation is perfect, and I have not hesitated to try and point out the faults and weaknesses which existed side by side with the very great achievements. The book does not pretend to be a history or a full account of Great Western locomotive design. It is rather what the sub-title says, 'A Critical Appreciation'. When I was in Swindon Works in the mid-1920s there was a self-satisfied complacency and arrogance about the place which was as ridiculous as it was infuriating. The general attitude seemed to be that everything the GWR did was right and marvellous, and that nothing done by other railways was any good at all. I was told in all seriousness by responsible men that 'the other railways never gave their engines a proper overhaul like we did' and that 'the Southern King Arthurs were rotten engines, no use whatever'. This attitude seemed usual with all ranks. In those at the top it was a real menace, inhibiting improvement and progress in design, and leading to the perpetuation of serious faults and failings which could so easily have been put right.

Some readers may well ask 'Who is this fellow who dares to deride some of the things done by Dean and Collett, and even to criticise work done by the Master, Churchward himself?' I can only claim a lifelong 70-year study of the subject, from the time when as a three-year-old living almost underneath the bridge over the Severn which led into Shrewsbury station I learned my first important lessons. I was taught by my father to distinguish between green Great Western engines and London & North Western ones which were black, also between tender and tank engines. The sheds were in my father's parish and among my first friends were drivers and firemen. Ever since, a large proportion of my friends have been railwaymen, and especially enginemen. What I owe to the great personal friendship I enjoyed with the late Harold Holcroft will become evident to anyone who reads this book. He was Churchward's 'bright young man' in the Swindon drawing office from 1907, when he was taken out of the normal gang system to become in effect a one-man gang for any special task demanding initiative and imagination. On Churchward's direct instructions he personally designed the famous 43xx moguls, the pioneers of the modern mixed-traffic locomotive. Many of the details which remained standard practice until the end of Great Western steam, were originated by him. He moved to the South Eastern & Chatham Railway under Maunsell in 1914; later, on the formation of the Southern Railway, he was technical assistant, first to Maunsell and then to Bulleid. As such he exercised considerable influence behind the scenes, as he himself described it, 'the tail wagging the dog'. He was a brilliant designer of locomotives and an exceptionally kindly and generous man.

I was perhaps fortunate in starting my apprenticeship in the Works of the Midland & South Western Junction Railway at Cirencester. There one found no belief at all in the doctrine of 'Swindon Infallibility', and surprisingly the standards of maintenance, workmanship and finish were on the whole considerably higher than those of the Great Western. They were in fact so high as to be uneconomic in the changed circumstances after the 1914–18 War. I therefore went to Swindon with an open mind, ready to be critical where criticism was deserved, whereas if I had been there from the beginning I might have caught the usual attitude of blind adulation.

I worked on many of the engines, and have since driven some of them, shunting and with loose-coupled goods trains. This book is written mainly from the point of view of the men who had to maintain and run the engines, especially drivers, firemen and fitters. They are the people who soon discover any faults in design the hard way, by having to cope with them. I hope that many readers will have or obtain H. Holcroft's excellent book *An Outline of Great Western*

Locomotive Practice 1837–1947. It is, I believe, still obtainable in paper-back. In a sense my book may be described as a commentary on the history of which Holcroft's work is such an admirable outline. Another very useful work to be able to refer, as I have done very frequently, is the Railway Correspondence & Travel Society's set of volumes *The Locomotives of the Great Western Railway,* to which I am greatly indebted. This work would be of even greater value if the writers had not been so obsessed with every tiny detail and minor variant of boilers, to the neglect of other and more important features. Boilers cannot and need not be built exactly to size by fractions of an inch, and it does not matter in the slightest if an engine has 228 small tubes in the boiler or 230. On the other hand, valve travel and lap, port sizes and the like, can make all the difference in the world to efficiency and economy, and the type of safety valve used is of far more significance than the shape or height of the safety valve bonnet. It is for such details that one searches in vain in the RCTS series. Nevertheless, the books remain a very valuable account of the various classes of locomotive, the variations within classes, and the sort of work for which they were used. I for one am very grateful to the Society and the writers.

While at Swindon, I was fortunate in learning the truth about certain mistakes and failures, which were so successfully hushed-up that no one else living today seems to know about them, or if they do they have kept it quiet. These revelations add, I think, a certain relish to the dish I am able to offer.

Finally, in suggesting that from time to time the civil engineering department, responsible for track and bridges among other things, was deceived over the real weight of some engines, I am not inferring that there was any danger to the public. Railway civil engineers were notoriously over-cautious, and often imposed unreasonable restrictions on the locomotive designers. It sometimes seemed that this was more a matter of the enjoyment of power over another department than any real necessity. There was always an ample margin of safety to cover a little extra weight, though track maintenance costs might be slightly increased.

John C. Gibson

1
The Genius of Gooch

Great Western locomotive design got off to a magnificent start with the work of Daniel Gooch, the first locomotive superintendent. Gooch's achievements were all the more remarkable in that he was appointed a few days before his 21st birthday on 18 August 1837.

He began his appointment facing exceptional difficulties. While locomotives for short-distance coal traffic had been built for some 20 years they were primitive contraptions, such as the Hetton Colliery locomotive which is still in existence. They were only expected to run at about 8mph. The art of designing and building engines for passenger haulage, at speeds up to 30mph or even 40mph was only just beginning. No-one except the Stephensons, with their improved Rockets such as *Northumbrian* and their pioneer inside-cylinder engines of the Planet type, had much experience of designing and building engines for main line work.

Gooch was landed with an almost impossible situation in that before his appointment a number of engines had been ordered of absurd and freakish design, most of which proved to be quite useless. They had been constructed to specifications drawn up by Brunel, who was Gooch's boss, and the man to whom he owed his appointment. Gooch was expected to run a train service with these monstrosities, yet to find fault with them was to criticise his superior. This must have been a terribly difficult position, both mechanically and diplomatically, especially for so young a man at the threshold of his career. That Gooch coped and survived is a remarkable tribute to his stature, both as an engineer and as a man of affairs.

It must be remembered that at this time there was no recognised profession of mechanical engineering. Engineers were simply classed as military or civil. Hence the term 'civil engineer' for one concerned with structures, bridges, road beds and the like.) George Stephenson and his son Robert had very successfully combined the arts of both civil and mechanical engineering, but they were exceptional.

Broad gauge 2–2–2 *Fire Fly*, Gooch's first design, and the first real express engine in the world

Isambard Kingdom Brunel was a civil engineer of outstanding genius, but his knowledge and experience of locomotives was virtually nil. As engineer-in-chief of the Great Western Railway he was responsible for all branches of engineering — that is why he chose and appointed Gooch, and remained his superior. Brunel's ideas of steam engines were probably derived mainly from pumping engines, with which he would have had experience in connection with his work on the Thames Tunnel and other civil engineering projects. These would have been large and ponderous beam engines, operating at very slow speeds indeed. As a result, Brunel was obsessed with the idea that an extremely low piston speed was essential. In his specification issued to a number of engine builders, he had insisted on a very low piston speed, and an impossibly low weight.

In their attempts to comply with an impracticable specification the unfortunate builders had to resort to huge driving wheels, to keep piston speed low, and they took up much of the scanty weight allowed. In an attempt to reduce weight they had to use very small

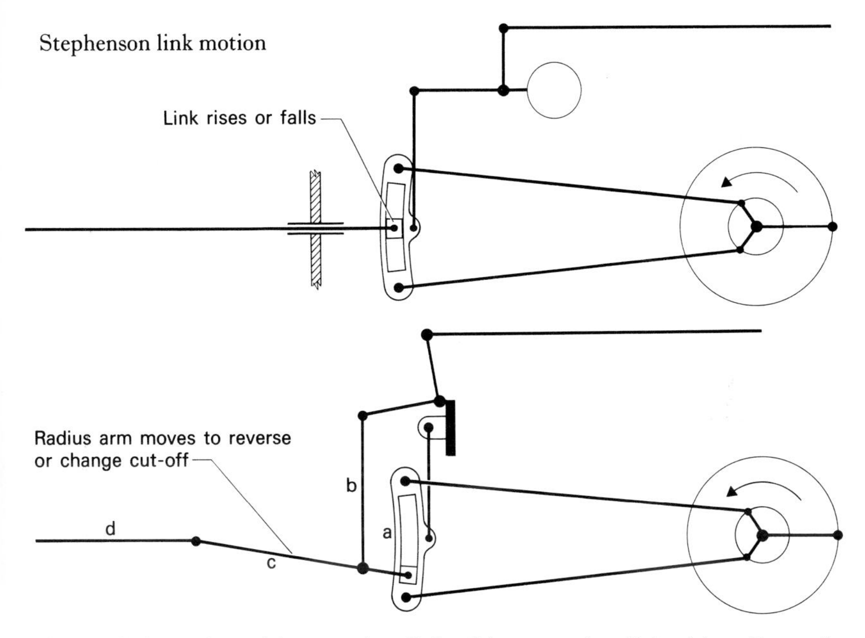

Stephenson link motion

Gooch link motion: (a) expansion link, (b) suspension link, (c) radius rod, (d) valve spindle

boilers, and even then the stipulated weight was exceeded by around 50 per cent. One is reminded of Dugald Drummond's remark made some 45 years later when he took up his duties as locomotive superintendent of the Caledonian Railway. Referring to some of the engines that he inherited, he described them as 'Like skinny chickens, all legs and wings'.

The majority of the engines built to try and meet Brunel's specification had 8ft 0in driving wheels and about 500sq ft of heating surface but one, *Ajax*, had 10ft 0in driving wheels and even less heating surface. 'All legs and wings' indeed. Of the 17 engines of this type, only *Vulcan* seems to have done much real work. This was the very first to be delivered, and hauled the directors' special which was run a few days before the opening of the line from London to Maidenhead. The line was nearly level, and the train was doubtless extremely light, otherwise it is questionable whether such an engine could have managed to get it along. A similar engine, *Aeolus*, pulled the first public passenger train on the opening day, and is reputed to have made very heavy weather of it.

The other two attempts to meet Brunel's specification were real freaks. Both were built by R. & W. Hawthorn, and were attempts to solve the weight problem by mounting engine and boiler on separate carriages. They were made under a patent of T. E. Harrison. One of them, *Thunderer*, was an 0–4–0 so far as the engine portion was concerned, with 6ft 0in coupled wheels geared up in the ratio of 27:10. This was the equivalent of 16ft 3in driving wheels. The engine not surprisingly was a complete failure. It appears to have done no work at all, apart from trial trips, and was reported as 'Engine sold, boiler used for stationary engine'. One wonders who bought the engine and what he made of it, unless it was sold as scrap, which seems likely.

The other engine, *Hurricane*, was not quite such an oddity, in that the engine portion was a 2–2–2, with 10ft 0in driving wheels. (The boiler of each engine was carried on a 6-wheeled truck. One can imagine much trouble with the flexible pipes of the period.) This engine was also a complete failure, but its boiler, and possibly some other parts, were used in building the 0–6–0 goods engine *Bacchus*, which ran from 1849 to 1869, and seems to have been quite satisfactory. All these locomotives were for the Great Western Railway's broad gauge, 7ft 0¼in.

With such a motley collection of locomotives, it is not surprising to read that for months Gooch lived in a carriage in the engine shed, working often day and night to try to get some service from the engines. The situation was just saved by a fortunate accident.

The Stephensons had built two engines of a very sound and orthodox 2–2–2 type for the 5ft 6in gauge New Orleans Railway in the United States. As often seems to have happened, no money was forthcoming, and the engines were left on the builders' hands. Gooch, who had worked as a draughtsman for the Stephensons for a time, snapped them up. *North Star* was delivered by barge to Maidenhead after being hastily altered to broad gauge in good time for the opening of the first section of the line. It was the only reliable performer that the company had for a time, and one can only suppose that it shuttled back and forth between London and Maidenhead almost continuously day after day. The other engine built for New Orleans, *Morning Star*, came nearly a year later, and was followed by ten others of generally similar design, delivered over a period of about two years, and all named after stars.

Faced with such an impossible situation, Gooch acted with great energy and skill, and quickly produced his first design, the Fire Fly class. These locomotives were outstanding in many ways. They can fairly be considered the first real express engines to be built anywhere in the world. I know of no other class of the period that could and did achieve a speed of 60mph. It was much the largest class to be built in that early period, comprising 62 engines; 17 were delivered in the year 1840 alone, and the rest had followed by the end of 1842. They were also believed to be the first attempt in any branch of engineering at real standardisation and interchangeability of parts. The locomotives were built by seven different firms. To each of these Gooch sent specifications, drawings, patterns and templates to ensure standardisation, and it is reported that he took a very firm line with any builder which failed to conform. This standardisation and use of templates and patterns was in itself a great step forward, a remarkable testimony to the practical forethought and breadth of view of this still very young man.

The Fire Fly class locomotives in themselves were virtually enlargements of *North Star*. In this again, Gooch showed his commonsense and sound judgement. To use the most satisfactory class of engine the company possessed as a foundation on which to build was a very wise move. A basic feature of *North Star* which was followed in most subsequent broad gauge engines, except for a few built in the 1860s mostly under Joseph Armstrong, was the sandwich frame. This consisted of two iron, later steel, plates, which were quite thin, 3/8in or 1/2in, with oak blocks some 4in or 5in thick between them, the whole being fastened together with bolts and nuts. Harold Holcroft has an interesting description of the making of a pair of these frames at Wolverhampton Works, in which he assisted as late as about 1900. (*Locomotive Adventure* Vol 1).

The sandwich frame construction had certain advantages over both plate and bar frames, particularly on the baulk road used by Brunel, and retained over much of the Great Western until the end of the century. This was composed of bridge rails fixed to very massive longitudinal baulks of timber, and was much more rigid and gave a harder ride than cross-sleepered track. The oak packing seemed to absorb the resultant vibration to a very useful degree. These frames also had some lateral flexibility, very desirable in the days before bogies, pony trucks and radial axleboxes came into vogue. They do not seem to have been liable to the cracking which bedevilled plate frames right up to the end of steam, particularly on the Great Western and the LNWR, and subsequently on the LMS. All Churchward's locomotives, as we shall see later, suffered continually from frame breakage, as did the otherwise excellent LMS 'Black Fives' to a lesser extent.

The performance of the Fire Fly class was exceptional for those days. Paddington to Exeter by the 'Great Way Round' via Bristol was a distance of some 194 miles. At first the booked time for the run was five hours, but the engines seem to have managed this so easily that it was soon cut to 4½ hours, an average speed of just over 42mph, including five stops. The running average must have been more like 47mph or 48mph. Such averages were not attained anywhere else in the world until some 15 years later. This was all the more remarkable as link motion had not then been invented, and the Fire Flies had the old 'gab' motion, with two hooks or gabs to engage the pins on the valve rods. This meant that the engines could not be linked-up to use the steam expansively. It is surprising that steam pressure could be maintained on these long fast runs, with the engine in full gear all the time. The boilers must have been remarkably good. The 'haystack' firebox with which they were fitted gave ample steam space just where it was most needed, right over the inner firebox where most of the evaporation took place, and this was probably a great help.

At this time the rival claims of the 7ft 0¼in and 4ft 8½in gauges were a subject of great controversy. The Government set up a Gauge Commission to study and report on the matter. Trials were held to assess the comparative speed and hauling power of the broad and standard gauge engines. The broad gauge was represented by *Ixion*, one of Gooch's Fire Flies, which proceeded to out-class the best standard gauge engines that the Northern lines could produce. The standard gauge people grew so desperate that they are said to have attempted to sabotage *Ixion*, and resorted to filling boiler and tender of their champion with boiling water from a stationary plant. Injectors had not then been invented, crosshead-driven pumps were almost universal, so there was no great problem in feeding the boiler with very hot water.

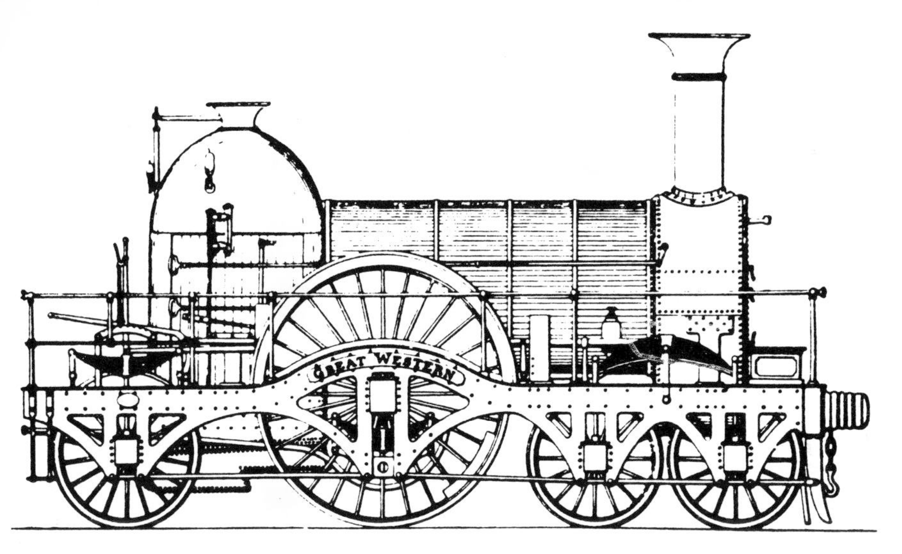

Broad gauge 4–2–2 8ft single *Great Western*, originally built as a 2–2–2, the first engine built at Swindon

Altogether, the Fire Flies were a triumph for young Daniel Gooch but some credit must no doubt be given to Thomas Russell Crampton, Gooch's chief draughtsman. Crampton later became famous for his own particular type of express engine, with large single driving wheels behind the firebox. They never really caught on in Great Britain, but became so popular on the continent that in France *prenez le Crampton* became a stock phrase for going by train. Some of the French Cramptons lasted into the twentieth century. Crampton was also ahead of his time in recognising the need for efficient valve events, using long travel and large direct steam ports at a very early date. In this he foreshadowed the work of Churchward 50 years later.

The Fire Flies were officially stated to have had a working pressure of 50lb/sq in, raised a little later on. In view of their performance one suspects that the true pressure was considerably higher from the beginning. In those days there was much public alarm over high pressures, and some engineers found it diplomatic to state a lower figure than the real one. Later on, when Archibald Sturrock left Swindon to become locomotive superintendent of the Great Northern Railway, Gooch is said to have privately advised him to use 150lb/sq in but to keep it a secret and state the pressure as 120lb/sq in. The Salter spring-balance safety valves then widely used could easily be screwed-down by the enginemen when no one was looking, and in view of the considerable number of boiler explosions on broad gauge engines in the early days, it seems likely that this practice was fairly common on the GWR at that time.

Successful as the Fire Flies were, much greater things were to come. Still worried by the Gauge Commission's findings, and anxious to emphasize the superiority of the 7ft gauge, the GWR directors authorised Gooch to produce locomotives of a size and power far in advance of anything built up to that time. The result was the introduction of the broad gauge 'Eight Footers', which were so far ahead of their time that they sufficed to run the West of England expresses right up to the final abolition of the broad gauge in 1892. By that time they had been slightly modified, with somewhat higher boiler pressures, steam and vacuum brakes, and cabs, but were basically of the same design. The original 30 were withdrawn between 1871 and 1888, and 24 replacements to much the same design built in those same years. The last four had active lives of only four years before the broad gauge was completely abolished. It is a great testimony to the original design that it should have been considered worthwhile to build engines of the class up to 40 years after their introduction.

The first to be built was experimental, and differed from the rest in various ways. This was the aptly named *Great Western*, the first engine to be built at the Swindon Works in 1846. (Broad gauge engines, being considered aristocrats, were not demeaned by being given numbers. Even the goods and tank engines were known by name only. Numbers were alright for the 'inferior' standard gauge engines.) *Great Western* as first built was a 2–2–2, with a very large haycock firebox. The firebox heating surface alone was 150sq ft, half as much again as the majority of engines had 50 years later.

Soon after it was built, *Great Western* went from London to Exeter in a running time of 208 minutes for the 194 miles, and also ran the slightly uphill 77 miles to Swindon in 78 minutes, with 100 tons behind the tender. It was many years before such speeds were attained anywhere else in the world. Not surprisingly for such a large engine, the weight on the leading axle proved to be too great, and axle breakage occurred. The engine was then rebuilt with longer frames as a 4–2–2 with rigid wheelbase, but as the two leading axles were only 4ft 4in apart the 19ft 0in fixed wheelbase was not excessive with a gauge of 7ft 0in. With the slight 'give' allowed by the sandwich frames, no trouble seemed to be experienced on curves, either with *Great Western* or its successors, which had much the same fixed wheelbase.

The following twenty-nine 8ft 0in singles, known as the Iron Duke class, were basically of the same design, with the 4–2–2 wheel arrangement. The boilers were rather longer, and the haycock firebox was discarded in favour of the raised round-topped box, which became a feature of many Great Western engines right up to the end of the century, until it was replaced by the raised Belpaire type. Another great improvement which was introduced on *Great Western* and continued on others was the replacement of the gab motion by Gooch's stationary link gear. It seems uncertain whether this was designed by Daniel Gooch or by his brother Joseph, at that time locomotive superintendent of the London & South Western Railway. Possibly it was really evolved by Crampton because very often a superintendent was given the credit for his chief draughtsman's work. Anyway, the fitting of this valve gear was a very great step forward, as it made linking-up and expansive use of the steam possible, with a great gain both in sustained power and economy.

The Stephenson or Howe shifting link motion had been introduced by the northern builders only a short time before, and it is possible that the Gooch brothers tried to obtain the same results, while avoiding any infringement of Stephenson patents. On the face of it, the Gooch arrangement seems the more logical. In Stephenson's gear the valve rod is held firmly, either by passing through a circular or rectangular guide, or being suspended by parallel links. To reverse the engine, or shorten the cut-off in forward gear, the whole complex of links, eccentric straps and rods has to be lifted and some friction between eccentric straps and sheaves overcome, necessitating balance weights or springs. In the Gooch gear the links are supported by hangers, and held at a more or less constant height. The die block is attached to a radius rod, the other end of which is connected to the valve spindle, so only the much lighter radius rods have to be raised and lowered.

In practice, the Stephenson gear proved superior. The pull and push of the eccentrics act more or less on the centre line of the valve gear, and the die block is rigidly held. In the Gooch gear the die block is not so rigidly held, and as full gear is approached the eccentric rods and the radius rods act at a considerable angle to each other. This results in much more slip of the block up and down the link all the time the engine is in motion, than with the Stephenson gear. Also, while the lead is constant with Gooch's gear, with properly designed Stephenson gear the lead increases as the engine is notched-up, a desirable feature as notching-up usually co-incides with increased speed. As Harold Holcroft has put it, with Stephenson's gear you get an effect somewhat analogous to advancing or retarding the ignition in a petrol engine, a very necessary procedure with a motor car or a motorcycle.

The Gooch link motion was rarely used in this country other than by the Gooch brothers themselves, but for some reason became widely used on the European continent. On the other hand, Stephenson's gear became almost universal, lasting practically to the end of steam on British Railways. Curiously enough, the GWR was the last to use it for main line locomotives, such as the 4–6–0 County class. Elsewhere, and on the GWR 4-cylinder locomotives, Stephenson's gear was generally superseded by Walschaert's early in the 20th century. Nevertheless, the introduction of either link motion was a great advance in the 1840s, possibly the biggest single improvement from the invention of the blastpipe until steam was discarded.

Apart from this great advance in design, the Gooch 8ft 0in singles were huge engines for their day. A great stir was caused in 1896 when McIntosh on the Caledonian Railway introduced his famous Dunalastairs in which the boiler diameter was increased from the then customary maximum of 4ft 5in to 4ft 9in. These quite small 4–4–0s have been hailed in the technical press as the beginning of the 'big engine era'. Yet the Iron Dukes had boilers 4ft 9¾in diameter, almost 50 years before the Dunalastairs appeared, and their total heating surface of nearly 2,000sq ft was about 30 per cent more, about equal to that of the LMS Stanier Class 5 and LNER 4–6–0s of the 1930s and 1940s. On the second batch of these engines, the Courier class built from 1848 onwards, the grate area was 25½sq ft, approaching that of the Saints, Stars, Halls, and well above the 20½sq ft of the Cities, the 4–4–0 Counties, 43xx moguls and others.

The 18in x 24in cylinders were not so big in proportion, but very large for their day. This size did not become usual elsewhere until about 1875. The published weight of the Couriers was 38 tons 4 cwt which seems suspiciously light for such big engines, with all the extra weight involved in having axles and cross-members longer and stronger to suit the 7ft gauge. It seems probable that this was an early example of cooking the weight diagrams to get by the civil engineer, a trick not unknown in the 20th century.

For a long time there was a persistent story around that one of the Couriers had run from Paddington to Didcot with a light train start to stop in 47 minutes for the 54 slightly uphill miles. Later generations discounted the story as very unlikely, if not impossible. However, some years ago a writer in *The Railway Magazine* stated that some correspondence had been found in which Gooch himself authenticated the feat, and he was a man renowned for his integrity. It is possible that the longitudinal-sleepered road while giving a hard and rather uncomfortable ride gave less rolling resistance than the normal cross-sleepered track where the rails can dip very slightly between supports, causing the train to climb in and out of countless very minute troughs all the time it is in motion.

Enough has been said to show that Gooch's express engines were as much ahead of their contemporaries as were Churchward's in 1905. Although these crack express engines naturally had most of the limelight, there were never more than 30 in service at any one time.

Gooch was responsible for many other classes, some smaller 2–2–2s, 2–4–0s, 0–6–0 tanks, and later on a class of rigid-frame 4–4–0s. The biggest class of over 100 for which he was responsible was his standard 0–6–0 goods. These were very large and powerful for their day, with 1574sq ft heating surface, grate area 19.2sq ft, and 17in x 24in cylinders. They were considerably larger so far as their boilers were concerned than most 0–6–0s of the 1880s, Dean Goods, Webb 'Cauliflowers' on the London & North Western, Johnson's numerous and famous 0–6–0s on the Midland, and so on.

A strange and ugly type for which Gooch was also responsible were the large and powerful 4–4–0 saddle tanks, which ran most of the passenger traffic in South Devon and Cornwall. Right up to the end of the broad gauge in 1892 they proved able to cope with the increasing train loads over the fearsome gradients.

The 4–4–0 tanks were unusual in that they used the boiler as a frame, traction engine fashion. The inside sandwich frames finished just ahead of the crank axle. The bogie, without side-play, was attached to a bracket riveted to the boiler barrel, by a ball-and-socket joint. This seems a crude arrangement, but at least the engines kept on the rails, unlike the 0–4–2 and 0–4–4 tanks with which Dean sought vainly to replace them for the West Country services. We shall be dealing with these later, and their fatal reluctance to stay on the track, in Chapter 3.

The broad gauge provided plenty of room for an adequate firebox and grate, and Gooch's boilers steamed well. On page 97 of his book *The Development of British Locomotive Design*, E. L. Ahrons states that he had it on good authority that H. A. Ivatt derived the idea for the wide firebox on his famous large Atlantics from the broad gauge engines. These in turn led to the wide fireboxes on all the numerous and successful Pacifics, which were the principal express engines on the LNER, LMS, and finally the Southern, right up to the end of steam.

So far, the account of Gooch's work has been an almost unbroken success story. What can we find to criticise? There was one design of his which was not very successful, his Metropolitan tanks.

When the first section of the Metropolitan Railway was built it was laid to mixed gauge so that it could be worked by the Great Western. Gooch had therefore to provide condensing engines, the first in the country, and the last locomotives designed by him before his retirement. They were 2–4–0 tank engines, with well tanks under the boiler and under the footplate. To leave room for the forward tank, the cylinders were placed outside on the 7ft gauge, which made the engines very wide indeed. The cylinders were steeply inclined, doubtless to clear the station platforms.

The idea of using well tanks appears to have been to keep the centre of gravity low, in the interest of stability. This seems to have been rather an obsession with locomotive engineers of the period. It was later to be found unnecessary and in fact harmful to the track, as it made cornering loads on the rails more horizontal than vertical, the direction in which rails are weakest. Tanks on condensing engines have to be frequently drained and re-filled, otherwise the water becomes too hot to condense the steam. This may well have been

Replacement 4–2–2 8ft single *Eupatoria*, built in 1878 with steam brake, vacuum equipment, and cab

another reason for having well tanks, which would be easier to drain into a pit between the rails than the saddle tanks normally used by Gooch.

The irony is that the Metropolitan soon fell out with the Great Western, and made other arrangements for working the trains. These rather mis-shapen engines therefore became surplus. The condensing gear was removed, and the engines were used to some extent on ordinary suburban work. They did not last very long, only about 10 to 12 years before they were scrapped. All 22 boilers, having had comparatively little use, survived for stationary work.

The only other criticism of Gooch's work that we can find is with regard to brakes. He was not alone, for nearly all locomotive engineers of the period seemed curiously indifferent to the need for stopping trains, whether in ordinary service or in emergencies. One is reminded of the famous car designer, Ettore Bugatti. Criticised for the very feeble brakes provided on his earlier sports cars he remarked, 'I design my cars to go, not to stop'. A similar attitude seems to have prevailed on railways, particularly in Great Britain.

Typical broad gauge 0–6–0 goods engine designed by Gooch, of the 1850s

Until about the 1870s brakes were fitted on tenders only, the engines being without any brakes at all. Gooch made this far worse by providing brake hangers and blocks on one side of the tender only. The wooden brake blocks of the period had extremely short lives anyway, and to halve the number must have made this weakness much worse. It also imposed twisting strains on the axles, the more so because the broad gauge axles had to be that much longer.

On his earlier 4–4–0 tanks Gooch used sledge brakes, bearing down on the rails instead of pressing on the wheel rims. When applied at all hard, they necessarily raised the engine, relieving the wheels of much of their load. This naturally resulted in derailments, particularly at points and crossings, and the sledges had soon to be replaced with the normal arrangement of hangers and blocks.

Towards the end of Gooch's time as locomotive superintendent, the absorption by the Great Western of the Shrewsbury & Birmingham, the Shrewsbury & Chester, and some other lines in the North, meant that there was a considerable mileage of standard gauge for which provision had to be made. Gooch therefore designed three classes of engine for the 4ft 8½in lines, a 2–2–2, a 2–4–0 and an 0–6–0. These were of very similar design to the broad gauge engines, though somewhat smaller. They all had outside sandwich frames, raised round-top fireboxes, and Gooch stationary link motion, except for the 2–4–0s, which rather surprisingly had the Stephenson shifting link motion, as did the later 157 Class of 2–2–2s. These last were designed by Gooch, though built by Sharp Stewart & Co.

There is no doubt that Sir Daniel Gooch, as he became later, was one of the greatest locomotive superintendents of the whole age of steam. He retired in 1864 at the early age of 47. He may well have been disappointed by the inevitable decline of the broad gauge, which could now be clearly foreseen. After leaving the Great Western, Gooch took a major part in laying the first trans-Atlantic telegraph cable with Brunel's huge ship, *Great Eastern*. It was for this work he was made a baronet. By this time the Great Western Railway was stagnating, and getting into financial difficulties. The board had such confidence in Gooch that they recalled him, and elected him chairman. His wise and firm leadership soon restored the situation, and he remained chairman until his death. Sir Daniel Gooch was not only a great engineer, he was also a very great man.

2 The Armstrongs

This chapter can be fairly brief, but not because the contribution of the Armstrong brothers, Joseph and George was unimportant — far from it. Their designs were so very sound that there is little if anything to be said in criticism, and so orthodox that there is not a great deal to be said in appreciative comment.

First some explanation is needed as to why we speak of the Armstrongs in the plural. The fact is that at this period, from the resignation of Gooch in 1864 until the death of Joseph Armstrong in 1877, the Great Western was in a state of rapid evolution, from broad gauge to a mixed gauge system (employing a third rail common to both gauges), and then to a mainly standard gauge line, with only the lines in Devon and Cornwall remaining unmixed broad gauge until 1892. By about 1878 only the through trains to the far West and the local trains west of Exeter had to be for the 7ft gauge.

At the beginning of the Armstrong period, the Great Western was virtually two systems, the broad gauge in the south and west, and the narrow gauge, as the Great Western called standard 4ft 8½in gauge, in the north. The locomotive headquarters for the former was Swindon, under Joseph Armstrong, and for the standard narrow gauge, Stafford Road, Wolverhampton in charge of George Armstrong. Joseph, the elder brother was in overall command, but he gave George a very free hand, so that Wolverhampton practice came to differ in frame and boiler design as well in many details from that of Swindon. There was even a different livery, the Wolverhampton green being of a much bluer tinge; the frame colour, lining-out, and extent of polished brass also differed.

Standard gauge had begun to intrude on a purely broad gauge railway, when in 1854 the Great Western absorbed the Shrewsbury & Birmingham and the Shrewsbury & Chester, from the start both built to the 4ft 8½in gauge. These two had already amalgamated before the Great Western took over, and had established their locomotive works at Wolverhampton, with Joseph Armstrong in charge, and brother George as his assistant and works manager.

While still in charge at Wolverhampton under Gooch's overall authority Joseph Armstrong had occasion to build some engines to his own design, in replacement of some of the less satisfactory engines taken over from constituent companies. These showed that already some of his ideas were very different from Gooch's. In particular he preferred ordinary plate frames to sandwich frames, and Stephenson valve motion to Gooch.

When Gooch resigned as locomotive superintendent in 1864, Joseph Armstrong was appointed to succeed him. Unlike Gooch, he was also made responsible for carriages and wagons, and this arrangement continued under his successors right through until nationalisation. This added to the immense burden already laid on Armstrong, as amid all his other commitments he had the task of building entirely new carriage and wagon works at Swindon. Very large numbers of new locomotives and other rolling stock were required for the ever-growing standard gauge lines, and Armstrong undertook to have them all constructed and ready when needed without going to outside builders. Extensive alterations were also needed at Swindon locomotive works to cope with the ever-increasing proportion of standard gauge stock. There is little doubt that Joseph Armstrong literally killed himself with overwork. He died in harness at the age of 60, mourned by everyone from chairman to labourer. He had not only served the company with untiring devotion, he had also worked unceasingly for the welfare of his men and their families, and the then almost entirely GWR town of Swindon.

Armstrong certainly had no time for messing about with eccentric and sometimes lunatic experimental designs, as his successor Dean did. It is very unlikely that he would have wanted to anyway. As the circumstances of the time required, he concentrated on designing and building very sound, conventional, standardised types of locomotives to meet all the various needs of a large and growing system. Gradually his designs became even more conventional and were none the worse for that. I know of none which was unsuccessful, and most were of such excellence that they were the foundation of all the Great Western standard gauge designs until Churchward's revolution from 1902 onwards. Moreover engines of this school of design were revived under Collett and built in very large numbers, over one thousand 0–6–0 tanks being built from 1929 onwards, among other classes of basic Armstrong origin.

I have already said that Armstrong adopted normal plate frames, abandoning the sandwich pattern, and used Stephenson valve gear instead of Gooch gear. Further moves towards conventional design were the eventual abandonment of raised fireboxes, and the introduction of domes. The domes in effect took the place of the raised fireboxes used by Gooch, by making up for the lost steam space, and bringing the entry for steam to the regulator even higher above the water line.

Let us now look at Joseph Armstrong's more important designs, and see how remarkably successful they were. First the crack express engines, the 2–2–2s, mainly used on the Birmingham and Wolverhampton expresses. The West of England main line was still looked after so far as the expresses were concerned by the Gooch broad gauge eight-footers. The 30 Sir Daniel class locomotives built from 1866 to 1869 set the pattern for all subsequent GWR 2–2–2s. They were a very sound, conventional design with double plate frames, a longish wheelbase, adequate boiler power for the period, and conventional inside cylinders and motion.

Their slightly larger successors of very similar design, the Queen or Sir Alexander class of 21 engines, aided by another ten added by Dean (the 157 class) sufficed for the Wolverhampton expresses right up to about 1901. It was only at the turn of the century that the installation of larger turntables made it possible to use eight-wheeled engines, 4–2–2s and 4–4–0s, on the Northern main line. The 157 class were almost identical to the Sir Alexanders, except that in them Dean reverted to sandwich frames.

To return to the Sir Daniel class. When by the end of the century their adhesion weight was proving inadequate for the heavier trains, Dean rebuilt 23 out of the 30 as 0–6–0 goods engines, giving them a further lease of life and usefulness. This was a genuine rebuild, not a replacement. Cylinders and motion were already standardised as between the 2–2–2s and the 0–6–0s, another instance of Armstrong's common sense in design. They could be and were used again, with some adjustment of cylinder angle. The old frames were used, with large patches riveted on at the middle, to bring the driving horn gaps

Armstrong 2–2–2 No 1131 of the Queen class, as altered by Dean with domed boiler, closed splashers, and cab

down to a height suitable for the much smaller driving wheels, 5ft 1in instead of 7ft 0in. As altered, these engines corresponded very closely to Armstrong's Standard Goods, the next class with which we have to deal. As rebuilt, some of the Sir Daniels served for a number of years, the last being withdrawn in 1920. Others were scrapped quite soon, but that was not because they were faulty.

By that time the 'new broom' Churchward was very much in charge. He did not seem to have approved of engines without guiding wheels. Churchward designed no 0–6–0s, building instead first the inside-cylinder Aberdare 2–6–0s and later on the versatile 43xx mixed-traffic 2–6–0s, and the 2–8–0s for the heavier work.

In 1866 Armstrong produced the first of his Standard Goods, a most successful design of which no fewer than 310 were built in the next ten years. They were simple, rugged engines with adequate boiler power. It is interesting to note that their tractive effort was the same as that of the famous Dean Goods, first built in 1883, with the last batch coming out in 1899. Heating surface, grate area and total weight, all available for adhesion, were very nearly the same, too. This shows how well up to the needs of the time were the Standard Goods. Most of them survived until the 1920s, the last not being withdrawn until 1934. In their later years, nearly all were fitted with Belpaire boilers with pressures gradually raised from the original

Armstrong Standard Goods 0–6–0 No 782, as running in the early 1900s with Belpaire boiler

140lb/sq in to 150lb/sq in, then 165lb/sq in. A number were fitted with small superheaters from 1911 onwards, and some were equipped with top feed. Some of them lasted for 58 years, and were certainly a very good investment. The only significant difference between them and the later Dean Goods, was that they had double frames, which made them more expensive to build but more robust, with larger bearing areas for the all-important driving axles.

Twenty more engines, identical except for their smaller 4ft 6in wheels, were built for the Pontypool Road to Birkenhead coal traffic, and known as Coal Engines. When it is remembered that in those days Liverpool was the most important base for ocean liners, and that they burned Welsh steam coal, the importance of this traffic is obvious.

Probably the most notable of all Joseph Armstrong's designs, for longevity and useful service over a very long period of time, was the famous Metro 2–4–0 tank. These engines were built over a period of 30 years, from 1869 to 1899. During all that time and until the 36xx class 2–4–2 tanks appeared in 1902 they were the largest and most powerful tank engines that the GWR possessed, apart from a few oddities and freaks, of which more when we come to consider the régime of William Dean.

For many years the Metro tanks were responsible for nearly all the

London surburban traffic, many of them being fitted with condensing gear for working over the Metropolitan line, hence their official designation of Metropolitan tanks, usually shortened to Metro. Even after the introduction of much larger engines early in the 20th century, the Metros continued to do a good deal of the London suburban work. As late as 1929–30 when I was living in Maidenhead, a quite fast limited-stop train used to arrive every Sunday afternoon, pulled by one of the 'Get Wets'. Engines of this class fitted with condensing gear were still without cabs, having only weatherboards and sheets — hence the nick-name. The idea seems to have been that engines working for much of their time in tunnels, but by no means all, did not need cabs. I would have thought that sooty drips off tunnel roofs were even more to be guarded against than clean country rain, but Swindon seemed to think otherwise.

It was not until the 61xx class 2–6–2 tanks appeared in 1931, and the condensing version of the 0–6–0 standard pannier tanks in 1933, that the Metros finally lost their jobs in the London area. Meanwhile very many of the class without condensing gear and after about 1878 with cabs were used over much of the Southern area, particularly from Oxford, Bristol, Taunton and Gloucester. They not only

Metro 2–4–0 tank No 1417 in early state; one of the 'get wets' with condensing gear, short side tanks but no cab

worked the more important branches, but hauled fast trains between Gloucester and Cardiff, and similar centres. I remember them between 1911 and 1922 on passenger trains between Bristol and Trowbridge, Westbury, Chippenham, etc as I then lived in Bath. However, my most vivid recollection is of a holiday spent near Dulverton Station, where the Exe Valley line from Exeter joined the Taunton-Barnstaple line. The light trains to Tiverton and Exeter had Wolverhampton 0–4–2 tanks, but the heavier and faster Barnstaple trains had the rather larger Metros. The work they did over that very difficult line, all steep gradients, sharp curves, and with most of the stations in the 'dips', was amazing. They seemed so fast and powerful that when many years later I discovered how very moderate their dimensions were I found it very hard to believe.

The engines were modified over the years, with different boilers, higher pressures, and in some cases larger bunkers, with or without all-over cabs, but the basic design was Joseph Armstrong's of 1868. Most of them lasted well into the 1930s, and six of them survived to be taken over by British Railways in 1948. Theirs was a record of long and often arduous service, second to none.

Because of its decreasing mileage, Armstrong had little need to build more engines for the broad gauge. He was however responsible for beginning the reconstruction or replacement of the Gooch eight-footers, a programme completed under Dean. He also designed the Acheron class, interesting as an early example of what were later called mixed-traffic engines. These were 2–4–0s of moderate dimensions by broad gauge standards, and with comparatively small (6ft 0in) driving wheels when compared with other broad gauge engines other than the 0–6–0 goods. They were used mostly for passenger trains on the less important lines such as the Wilts & Somerset, while after the takeover of the Bristol & Exeter, South Devon, and Cornwall Railways in 1876, some of them were drafted to the West Country. Others were altered to saddle tanks with 5ft 0in driving wheels also for service in Devon and Cornwall. With 16in x 24in cylinders, 1,200sq ft heating surface, and a weight of 29½ tons, they were of average size for their period by the standards of other railways, but small by comparison with the broad gauge express engines, the big singles and the Waverley class 4–4–0s. However, they were useful engines on the work for which they were intended.

Armstrong also produced standard gauge 2–4–0 tender engines of several classes for secondary passenger services, but they call for no particular comment. He also began the provision of large numbers of 0–6–0 tank engines which were such a feature of the Great Western, built in quantity by Dean, and many years later by Collett.

To sum up, Joseph Armstrong seems to be the least known and remembered of all the Great Western locomotive superintendents. (They were not called 'chief mechanical engineer' until 1916.) Yet it is fair to say that he left the Great Western better provided with sound engines for every class of traffic than any other railway in Britain, and probably in the world. He does not appear to have produced a design which was not successful, which can be said of very few locomotive engineers, and his Metro 2–4–0 tanks must have been one of the most successful designs of all time for the work they were intended to do.

Meanwhile, George Armstrong at Wolverhampton was not idle. He built a few 2–4–0 tender engines, but nearly all his designs were for tank engines, for which he is justly famous. He produced a number of medium-sized 0–6–0 tanks of similar size and power to those built at Swindon under brother Joseph, and later Dean. These were different in many details from the Swindon types, although it is for the smaller sizes of tank engine that George Armstrong and the Wolverhampton Works became best known.

The smaller, lighter 0–6–0 tanks with 4ft 0in wheels were originally designed by George Armstrong, and 310 were built at Wolverhampton from 1874 until 1905. These small tanks have sometimes been called the 'Great Western Terriers', but small as they were they were considerably more powerful than the Stroudley Terriers on the Brighton line. A final 70, modernised in detail but basically similar, were built under Hawksworth, and not completed until after nationalisation.

However, George Armstrong's most brilliantly successful design was the 517 class 0–4–2 tank. It is interesting to notice that whereas Swindon passenger tanks were mostly 2–4–0s, those designed and built at Wolverhampton were all 0–4–2s. The latter were a good deal smaller than the Metro tanks, but they were intended for different jobs. In their earlier years they were responsible for most of the suburban traffic around the Birmingham and Wolverhampton dis-

Metro 2–4–0 tank in final form with overall cab and large bunker. The long side tanks leave no room for plate springs (*A. R. Brown*)

tricts, although with the very light 4-wheeled coaches then used, the smaller engines sufficed.

It was, however, on the innumerable branch lines which were such a feature of the Great Western system that these little tank engines came into their own. For this work they were ideal. Adequately powerful for the light trains, and with a surprising turn of speed when required, they were very economical, aided by their small 12sq ft grates which minimised stand-by losses. Later on in Churchward's time, many were adapted for push-pull working on the simple Great Western system, using universally jointed rods, which was much more reliable than the various vacuum, compressed-air or cable devices used elsewhere. In fact they became the standard engines for auto-train work, except in a few hilly districts where the small 0–6–0 tanks with 4ft 1½in driving wheels were preferred.

The class, totalling 164 engines, were all built between 1868 and 1885. No 1162 built in 1876 lasted until 1945, a life of 69 years. Many modifications were made over the years. The early examples built with short wheelbase, inside bearings for the trailing wheels, and saddle tanks, were all altered to resemble the later batches, with lengthened wheelbase, side tanks and outside bearings for the carrying axle. In later years many acquired Belpaire boilers, some had top-feed, and the pressure was gradually increased from the original 140lb/sq in, first to 150lb/sq in and then to 165lb/sq in.

By about 1930, however, most were getting past economical repair after an average life of 55 years, so they were scrapped. So useful and economical were they though that Collett built 95 new engines of the same basic dimensions and design; the 75 48xx (later 14xx) series were auto-fitted and there were 20 non-auto, Nos 5800–19. When this was done, some scoffed at this building of 'Victorian relics', but it was far more sensible than the LMS and British Railways custom of using 85-ton 2–6–4 tanks to pull branch trains of about 60 or 90 tons. In British Railways days, one of these lively little engines, 'by Collett out of George Armstrong', was timed at 80mph pushing one auto-coach. Two of these delightful little engines survive on the Dart Valley Railway, one is with the Great Western Society at Didcot, and yet another is a static exhibit in the Tiverton Museum in Devon. One of them starred in that excellent film of the early 1950s, *The Titfield Thunderbolt*.

3

William Dean — Phase One

When Joseph Armstrong died in office at the age of 60 in 1877, his chief assistant William Dean was appointed to succeed him. Dean was then 37, and his future and that of the Great Western locomotive, carriage & wagon department, seemed full of promise.

In the event, Dean's work was extraordinarily erratic. It reminds one of the little girl in the rhyme who '. . . when she was good she was very, very good, and when she was bad she was horrid!' In fact the saga of William Dean was a sad one. In his young days as an apprentice at Wolverhampton, he attracted notice by his intellectual gifts and his industry, and soon rose to be George Armstrong's right-hand man. In 1868 Joseph Armstrong brought him to Swindon as his chief assistant, to help with the enormous task laid on him by the rapid changeover to standard gauge. Dean was then only 28.

But the career which had begun so brilliantly ended with the complete failure of his mind by the time he was 60. Some of the crazier designs he produced during his reign as locomotive superintendent suggest that he must always have been a bit unbalanced. Eccentric genius is perhaps the fairest description we can find for him.

Dean's earlier efforts at design were both sensible and successful. His first express engines were the 157 class 2–2–2s, nominally rebuilds of a class of ten Singles built to Gooch's design by Sharp Stewart & Co in 1862, but really new engines, although the old wheels were probably used again, and possibly a few other parts. These new engines, popularly known as 'Sharpies' because of their supposed ancestry, were almost identical to Joseph Armstrong's Sir Alexander class, except that they had sandwich frames instead of plain plate frames. This was probably to give smoother running on the baulk road since most of the gauge conversion had been done by shortening the tie bars of the 7ft 0¼in gauge track, and moving one longitudinal sleeper with its bridge rail closer to the other one. This hard, unyielding road therefore persisted for many years as standard gauge. There was nothing to choose between the two batches of single-drivers in performance, and they shared the work on the Wolverhampton and Worcester lines until the turn of the century.

Dean next turned his attention to goods engines, and here he had his greatest success. The Dean Goods first built in 1883 were justly famous for generations. There were 260 of them in all, for though the numbers ran from 2301 to 2580, Nos 2361 to 2380 were a separate class, part of a scheme for a standardised set of Convertibles which we shall consider later. These 20 engines differed from the Dean Goods in having double frames, a longer wheelbase, longer boiler barrel and 26in stroke instead of 24in.

The Dean Goods proper were thus less numerous than Armstrong's Standard Goods, and as we have already noticed were of no larger dimensions. Yet they continued to be built as the standard goods engine until 1899, by which time they were rather small for the job. However, some happy combination of dimensions, the design of cylinders and valve gear, and the draughting turning out just right, ensured that they were unusually powerful and lively engines for their size. Their very light axle load for their power ensured their usefulness on lines that could not carry heavier weights, long after they were outdated for main line work. It was probably their high power-to-weight ratio and their reputation for reliability that led to the Government requisitioning 62 of them for service in World War I, and a further 100 in 1939.

The main difference between the Dean Goods and their Armstrong predecessors was that the former had inside frames only. At about the same period, the early 1880s, Dean resumed the building of 0–6–0 tanks, and here again double frames were abandoned. These engines, the 1813 class, were in fact a saddle tank version of the tender engines, using the same boiler, cylinders and motion, but with driving wheels 4ft 6in diameter, as against those on the Dean Goods, which were 5ft 0in. Their great importance lies in the fact that the 1813 class locomotives were the basis for several hundred locomotives built new from 1929 to as late as 1956. The last were similar to the 1813 class as modified by Churchward, with Belpaire boilers, pannier tanks in place of saddle tanks, and higher boiler pressure. The last 210, the 94xx class, had taper boilers, but below the running plate they were pure Dean.

Dean 2–2–2 No 158, as built with domeless boiler and open splashers. Note the sandwich frames

Both the 0–6–0 tender engines and the tanks were kept up-to-date under Churchward and Collett, with Belpaire boilers, and pressures rising in stages from 140lb/sq in to 180lb/sq in. Most of the tender engines and some of the tanks were superheated, though in the case of the tank engines the superheaters were later removed. It was found everywhere that for shunting superheating was ineffective and a nuisance in that it made the response to the regulator slower both in starting and in shutting-off steam. All Dean's 0–6–0 tanks, like most of Armstrong's, were built with round-topped saddle tanks, but nearly all were later converted to pannier tanks, which fitted better with the Belpaire fireboxes.

In their later days the Dean Goods proved invaluable on the Mid-Wales line of the Cambrian section, which could only take very light axle loads. It was in connection with this work that they had a late 'moment of glory'. After nationalisation the LMS-dominated locomotive department of BR wanted to replace the aged Dean Goods with new Ivatt LMS Class 2 2–6–0s. There was consternation in 'The Kremlin' — the British Railways Board headquarters at Marylebone — and jubilation in GWR circles when it was found that the new engines would not do the job effectively. Tests of both on the Swindon stationary test plant bore out the reports that the Ivatt engines would not steam as well as the venerable Dean 0–6–0s. The 2–6–0s and their very similar British Railways successors had to have alterations to the blastpipe and chimney, and it is fair to say that when they had been modified with draughting on the lines of the Deans they proved to be excellent little engines.

A grave fault in the first batches of Dean Goods and other engines built in the 1882–1887 period was the siting of the clackboxes on the firebox sides, the worst conceivable place to put the water feed from the injectors, but this was later remedied.

At about the same time as his successful efforts in designing tender and tank engines for goods traffic and shunting, Dean had to set about producing new designs of express passenger engines. In this he seemed to lose his way and foundered badly. His various wildly unsuccessful experiments must have cost the company a great deal of money to no purpose. It was perhaps fortunate for Dean that in those days there was no popular railway press, and the various failures attracted little attention, and could be hushed-up. Such public and professional interest as there was tended to be diverted to the antics of the much more numerous Webb Compounds on the LNWR.

For some curious reason Dean seemed obsessed with the idea of using tank engines for long-distance traffic. In the earlier years of his reign, much of the coal traffic from South Wales was hauled by saddle tanks, mainly of the Armstrong double-framed varieties, with lengthy pauses at almost every other water column. He seemed to think the same policy could work with express passenger trains, for all his early attempts were tank engines.

First, three double-framed 2–4–0 tender engines of Wolverhampton origin were converted to side tank engines. The water capacity was hopelessly inadequate for any long-distance work, but even so the weight turned out to be excessive. These engines were soon re-converted to tender engines.

Dean then tried again with No 1. It was a regular Great Western practice to use low numbers for experimental types, as we shall see again when we come to Churchward's early work. No 1 was a 4–4–0 tank engine. To lighten the axle loads and to increase the water capacity, the side tanks were extended right up to the smokebox tubeplate, which made the motion quite inaccessible without the aid of a pit. The real trouble lay with the bogie, which was of such an extraordinarily bizarre design that it almost looked as if poor Dean's sanity was already beginning to desert him. Dean at this stage seemed determined that bogies should not have centre pins. Why, one cannot

Dean Goods 0–6–0 No 2405, as built in 1891

imagine, unless it was a reaction against the too rigid bogies used on the South Devon saddle tanks designed by Gooch, which had no side-play whatever. In the case of No 1, the bogie was scarcely fixed to the frame at all. The only connection seems to have been through the spring hangers. The weight of the engine was hung on them by a frame on each side, shaped like a letter 'E' lying on its back. This frame was incredibly flimsy, being made of iron or possibly steel strips only about 3in deep, and 1in thick. This 'centreless' bogie was scarcely controlled at all. The spring hangers allowed it to move in any direction, restrained a little by the force of gravity as the hangers took up an inclination. Sideways however, there was virtually no restraint, as the flimsy E-frame just bent. It is unlikely that this nightmare engine ever entered service. As one would expect, it just refused to stay on the rails. Apart from the lack of control, the bogie had a very short wheelbase. This is always a bad feature, as such a bogie tends to take up an angle and proceed 'crabwise'.

The next experimental engine was such a disaster that officialdom at Swindon has from time to time tried to pretend that it never existed. It was No 9, a 4–2–4 single-driver tank engine of considerable size. Because of the desire to hush up this monstrosity, very few particulars have survived. Doubtless the drawings were quietly burned, and all we have to go on is a sketch made many years later by E. W. Twining, based presumably on reminiscences of old hands,

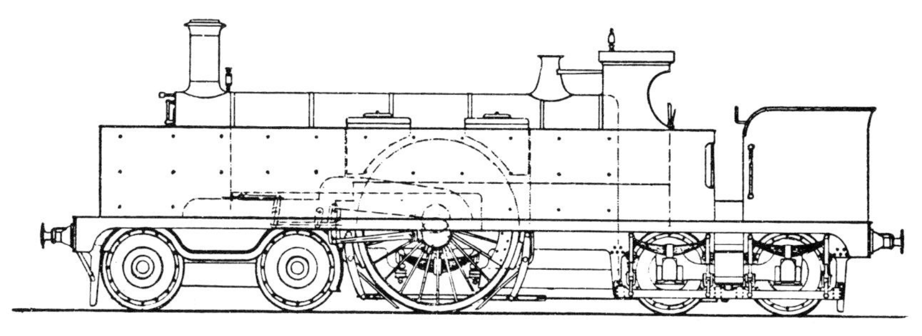

No 9 as a 4–2–4T (*E. W. Twining, courtesy Allen & Unwin*)

who probably did not dare to reveal anything until they had left the company's service.

The driving wheels were large, 7ft 8in diameter, the cylinders probably 18in x 26in, and the boiler domeless, large and long for the period. In an attempt to provide sufficient range of action, there was a large coal bunker with water tank under, and the side tanks extended well forward of the smokebox, almost to the buffer beam. Water capacity was said to be 2,500 gallons, about the same as the tenders then in general use. Large sandboxes were inserted in the tanks fore and aft of the driving wheels. To mitigate the inaccessibility of the motion hidden behind these lengthy tanks the eccentrics were mounted on the axle ends outside the wheels. The link motion was outside, and drove slide valves on top of the inside cylinders by means of rocking shafts. The trailing bogie looked as if it was taken just as it was from No 1, with all its glaring faults. Both bogies had Mansell wheels like many coaches of the time, with the space between hub and rim filled with wood blocks. No details of the front bogie have been revealed — the drawing shows wheels and mudguards, but nothing else. The wheelbase was rather longer than at the rear. One suspects that this bogie may have had a rigid pivot and no side play, but this is pure conjecture.

It is related that the great man himself, (for William Dean was very much the Victorian potentate at whose approach everyone trembled) came down from his eyrie to watch the 'engine of the future' steamed and brought out of the shops for the first time. In the works yard there stood a turntable, conveniently sited for engines entering or leaving the erecting shops. This 'masterpiece' managed, just, to get

Dean Goods 0–6–0 No 2524 in final form, with Belpaire boiler and superheater

as far as the turntable, then derailed and tumbled into the pit. Dean is said to have turned and walked away without a word, leaving his underlings to cope with the crisis. It is generally believed that this engine never did get as far as the main line. A number of Dean's designs were given to de-railing, as we shall see, but this was the worst of all. It never stayed on long enough to get anywhere. With no fixed wheelbase at all, and the rear bogie almost completely uncontrolled anyway, it is strange that anyone should have expected it to have any sense of direction, and to stay on the track. It didn't. After a lapse of some years, with the disgraced engine put in the corner under a sheet, the wheels and outside motion were used in an otherwise orthodox 2–2–2. We shall deal with this later, as it seems desirable at this point to interrupt the express engine saga, to deal with the needs of the broad gauge during its last years.

At this period, the 1880s, the broad gauge was, as Charles II said of himself, 'an unconscionable time dying'. It is usually believed that its life was prolonged until after Gooch's death to avoid upsetting him, for he was chairman of the board as well as the surviving hero from the pioneering days, Brunel being long since dead. One would have thought that Gooch was too sound an engineer, and too hard-headed a man of business to have acquiesced in this, but perhaps human vanity did outweigh commonsense in his last years. More probably there was a failure of communication between him and the board, each in their anxiety not to upset the other, misinterpreting their real wishes.

Be that as it may, it set the Locomotive, Carriage & Wagon Department a real problem. The broad gauge stock was old and worn out, yet trains had to be kept running, and no one would wish to build expensive new locomotives for an uncertain and very short life. So far as the express engines were concerned, Dean continued Armstrong's policy of replacing the 'Eight Footers' as they wore out, the last being built in 1888 for a life of only four years. To meet the needs of goods and tank engines, Joseph Armstrong had converted a number of his Standard Goods and saddle tanks, by putting the wheels outside the outside frames. This could quite easily be done with double-framed engines, and they could be re-converted to standard gauge without too much trouble when the time came. Following this example, Dean reverted to double frames for a standardised series of Convertibles, designed specially with easy conversion in mind. To this end, all the springs were underhung, giving them a unique and rather strange appearance when they were in standard gauge form. To this series belonged the 0–6–0s Nos 2361 to 2380, already mentioned when dealing with the Dean Goods proper. Using the same cylinders and motion, 5ft 1in wheels and similar springing arrangements, were some 2–4–0s, 2–4–0 tanks and 0–6–0 saddle tanks. The 2–4–0 tanks were found to have insufficient water capacity for their jobs, so were converted to 2–4–0 tender engines like the others. In the event the 0–6–0s always remained standard gauge engines, but a number of the other classes did run on the broad gauge for a few years.

For the purpose of this study in design, the main importance of this very sensible exercise in standardisation and versatility was this. It led Dean, who had gone in for inside-frame engines in a big way, to turn back to double frames, which he used from this time for nearly all his new designs, even where there was no need for convertability. Who knows, the Dukes, Flowers, Cities, Bulldogs and Aberdare 2–6–0s might never have been built with double frames

Former 0–4–2 tank rebuilt as a 4–4–0 tender engine with taper boiler, superheater and top feed; No 3525 passes Patchway

had this need for convertibles not arisen. Unlike every other main line in the country, the GWR never had any conventional inside-cylinder inside-frame 4–4–0s, which for a number of years became the standard British passenger engine. The only exceptions were a handful taken over from the Cambrian and the MSWJR at the Grouping.

I was employed on both double-framed Bulldog and on Midland & South Western 4–4–0s, and the latter were very much more accessible and convenient to work on. On trial trips they also gave a far smoother and more comfortable ride. The double-framed engines were heavier and more expensive to build and repair. Altogether it seems to have been a retrograde step to return to double frames other than for convertibles, which had to have outside frames, to become inside frames when they were altered to 7ft gauge.

The Dean Standard Convertibles mentioned on pages 42 and 43 seem to have been quite satisfactory in both guises, but Dean's next attempt to design a convertible was disastrous, producing more 'moving accidents looking for somewhere to happen!' These were 0–4–2 tanks of very curious proportions. The coupled wheelbase was very short, but the gap between the driving wheels and the trailing wheels was very long. Presumably to compensate for this long wheelbase, the trailing axleboxes were given complete freedom laterally, having no flanges to bear on the hornblocks. The spring hangers provided the only restraint on side movement. Side control was almost non-existent with such a flexible arrangement, with the natural result that the engines just would not stay on the track.

These engines, the 3521 class, were therefore rebuilt with trailing bogies, as 0–4–4 tanks. The coupled wheelbase still remained just as short, and unfortunately Dean again used a bogie with an extremely short wheelbase and very vague lateral control. With a bogie wheelbase of 4ft 6in, roughly equal to the 4ft 8½in gauge, they were none too safe in standard gauge form. Those that ran on the 7ft gauge were lethal. There was a serious accident at Doublebois in Cornwall, when a passenger train double-headed by two of these menaces derailed at speed. There were many less serious derailments, and some remedy had to be found.

What was done seems almost incredible. The 0–4–4 tanks were turned back to front as it were, and emerged from Swindon Works as 4–4–0 tender engines. By this time the broad gauge had vanished, so all the rebuilds were for the standard gauge. Swindon was always noted for astonishing reconstructions, but for broad gauge 0–4–2 tanks to finish up as standard gauge 4–4–0 tender engines was the most remarkable 'rebuild' ever. Actually, there cannot have been very much of the original engines left. Coupled wheels, cylinders and motion could be used again, but the frames must have been new, as the coupled wheelbase was longer. New and better bogies were used, with longer wheelbase and improved side control. More than half the class of 40 retained their small domed boilers, and had boilers of similar size with domes until the end; 14 were immediately fitted with Standard No 3 domeless boilers, as made for the 36xx 2–4–2 tanks. These were the same as those on Atbaras as built, except for a slightly shorter barrel. In due course these were replaced by the taper version, and in most cases ended-up with top feed and superheater. One suspects that these were rather heavy for the new frames which were of the antique sandwich type and very shallow. Presumably this was part of the 'window dressing', to try to 'con' directors and the management into thinking that they really were the original engines turned back-to-front, and conceal how much of the company's money had been wasted in building 40 engines in the first place to such a faulty design.

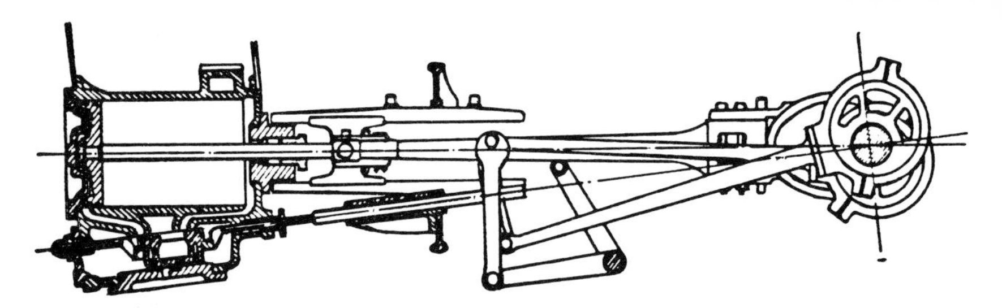

Dean's cylinder and valve arrangement as used on 7ft 8in singles, Atbaras, Cities, Bulldogs, Aberdares, etc.

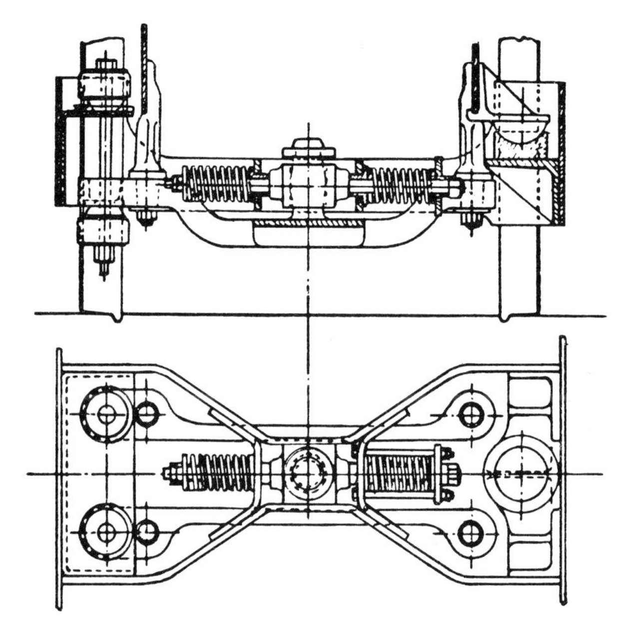

Dean's suspension bogie as used on 4–2–2 and 4–4–0 tender engines. The right hand side of the diagram shows the modification to the de Glehn principle by Holcroft in 1908 for the Flowers and Birds etc.

After the Grouping, I remained at the Cirencester Works of the MSWJR until it was closed in 1925. For some reason the GWR authorities took away a number of our simple and reliable 4–4–0s and gave us instead several of these 3521 class engines, the larger version with taper boilers. They gave a lot of trouble. I well remember one of them, No 3559, coming into Cirencester Works with hot driving axle boxes. All the underneath and sides of the boiler barrel were streaked in silver, where the white metal had become molten and been flung around. Another time I saw one of them trying to start a passenger train up the bank out of Cirencester station. It would not go, so the driver tried to set back. He could not move the reversing lever, so he called the fireman over to help. The two men struggled but were unable to shift it, so they summoned a porter from the platform and eventually it yielded to the efforts of the three men. I imagine both troubles were due to the very light and flimsy frames flexing, and the consequent loss of alignment causing binding. A contributory cause of the hot boxes may well have been the very small driving wheels for a 4–4–0, only 5ft 2in with new tyres. Our drivers were accustomed to 'let fly' down the long banks, and the little wheels would have had to revolve very fast indeed.

These horrors were soon removed, to our great relief, and our own 4–4–0s brought back, aided and abetted by two or three Dukes. Where the evil-doers went I do not know although they were by then beginning to go for scrap, but some lasted until about 1930. Before the Grouping, two of the smaller variety, with Dean Goods class boilers, were sold or lent to the Cambrian, which had smashed two of its all too few 4–4–0s beyond repair in the terrible head-on collision at Abermule in January 1921. I doubt if these engines improved the shocking punctuality record of the Welsh line.

4

William Dean — Phase Two

The 1880s was the period when compound locomotives came into fashion. On the London & North Western Railway Webb was turning out his 3-cylinder compounds in large numbers; T. W. Worsdell, having tried out a few 2-cylinder compounds on the Great Eastern, moved to the North Eastern and built them in quantity. Dean evidently thought he ought to have a go, and in 1886 built two 4-cylinder tandem compounds, Nos 7 and 8. Both had the cylinders inside, and looked conventional outwardly, except that the leading wheels were unusually far forward. No 7 was for standard gauge and had double frames. The 23in diameter low-pressure cylinders were mounted on the fronts of the 13in high-pressure cylinders, the two being one casting. The stroke was 21in. High- and low-pressure cylinders on each side were separated by a hollow casting which fitted outside the high-pressure cylinder and was fixed by studs, of which the nuts were inside the low-pressure cylinder. This casting had a bushed hole through which the common piston rod passed.

This engine did little work. The valve events were all wrong, with very limited cut-off at the back-end and excessive compression. The worst trouble was with the intermediate bush between the cylinders, which could not be lubricated satisfactorily, causing bad scoring of the piston rods. The engine ran slow trains between Swindon and Cardiff for a while. No one trusted it to work expresses. After being laid aside for several years, it was nominally rebuilt as 4–4–0 No 7 *Armstrong*, but probably only the coupled wheels were used again.

No 8 was for the broad gauge, and was really a convertible basically similar to No 7. The cylinder arrangement was rather different. The 22in diameter low-pressure cylinders were in front of the 14inch high-pressure. The partition between the cylinders was cast in one with the cylinder block, and no bush was needed as the low pressure piston had two rods which passed outside the high pressure cylinder to the common crosshead. This curious arrangement proved to be

Dean 7ft 8in single No 3028 as a broad gauge 2–2–2, at Paddington. It became standard gauge 4–2–2 *Wellington*

the engine's undoing. Ahrons in his *Locomotive and Train Working in the Latter Part of the Nineteenth Century* gives a delightful description of what happened the first and only time No 8 was set to haul an express from Bristol to Swindon. The running department played for safety by providing *Acheron*, one of Joseph Armstrong's broad gauge 2–4–0s of the Hawthorn class, as pilot. *Acheron*'s driver, one Jones, was instructed to give his engine just sufficient steam to move his own engine, so that it could be seen how No 8 would cope with a heavy train. Ahrons himself was on No 8's footplate, and must have had the fright of his life. All went reasonably well until they were climbing the 1 in 100 grade through Box Tunnel. Suddenly there was a fearful noise, an explosive outburst of steam, and a shower of cast-iron fragments and gunmetal nuts riccocheted off the tunnel roof and rained down on the footplate. As the cab roof was very scanty and there were four men on the footplate it was fortunate that no-one was 'shot'.

Driver Jones gave *Acheron* full steam and managed to keep the train moving until it was out of the tunnel. Jones was no doubt a

Welshman with the usual gift of tongues, for Ahrons says that listening to 'Jones on Compounds' was a feature of shed life for quite a while. What had happened was that three out of the four pistons had disintegrated and smashed the cylinder casting, many of the bits being shot out of the chimney, to rebound from the tunnel roof. No 8 did no more work, and was in the end nominally rebuilt as No 8 *Gooch*. That was Swindon's first and last attempt at building compounds. Next time the GWR authorities wished to experiment with compounding, they bought well-tried examples from France.

Dean seems to have been (as was said of a recent British Prime Minister) '. . . too clever by half' — highly ingenious but not very practical. We must not however suggest that his work at this period was all disastrous. While continuing to turn out his admirable if small Dean Goods and many sound 0–6–0 tanks, he also produced some excellent 2–4–0s. The 2201 class of 1881 and 3232 class of 1892 were plain, straightforward inside-framed engines, closely resembling each other. They were a development of Joseph Armstrong's 806 class, with only minor alterations. They were probably as good express 2–4–0s as any in the country. As a small boy living in Bath around 1911–12, I remember them working express trains turn and turn about with much larger and more modern Churchward engines. My father timed one at 80mph on a West-to-North express, Bristol to Shrewsbury via the Severn Tunnel, though I do not remember the location. It may well have been on the descent from Church Stretton.

Then there were the Barnums of 1889, a most interesting and successful class. They were more of a mixed-traffic type, having 6ft 1½in driving wheels, and in their early years were very useful working express trains on the heavily-graded Weymouth line, also to South Wales via Gloucester. They had larger cylinders and a longer firebox than the other 2–4–0s, so that they were considerably more powerful. They must have been designed with a view to possible conversion to broad gauge, as they were of the usual convertible type with outside frames and underhung springs. A return was made to sandwich frames, with the underhung springs within the sandwich. They were never converted, but in 1888 Dean had built two similar but larger convertibles with 7ft driving wheels, which remained broad gauge engines throughout their brief four-year lives. They were Nos 14 and 18, and were nominally rebuilt in 1894 as the other two members of the Armstrong class 4–4–0s.

We must now return to Dean's attempts to produce a satisfactory design for a first-rank express engine. After the fiasco with No 9 he went back to tender engines and produced two experimental singles. No 9 was officially a rebuild of the disastrous 4–2–4 tank engine. The driving wheels and the outside motion were used again, doubtless the cylinders as well. Bogies were discarded, and the engine was a 2–2–2 with outside bearings for the carrying wheels, but inside ones only for the driving wheels. The boiler was new and a good deal shorter than that on the tank engine.

A generally similar engine, No 10, appeared two years later in 1886. However, that had outside bearings throughout, and inside Stephenson gear driving slide valves underneath the cylinders direct, without rocking shafts. This engine is very important historically, as it was the first to have this arrangement of valves and motion, which was afterwards used in the 7ft 8in singles, all the inside-cylinder 4–4–0s, including the famous Cities, and in the Aberdare 2–6–0 goods engines.

Directly-operated valves beneath the cylinders were becoming very popular at about that time, having been used first by Stroudley on the LB & SCR, and taken up by James Holden on the Great Eastern for all his larger engines, including Claud Hamilton 4–4–0s. There was an advantage with slide valves that the valves could drop slightly off their seats when steam was shut-off, allowing free coasting, and avoiding a partial vacuum in the cylinders which could suck grit down from the smokebox. With the increasing size of cylinders, the normal British arrangement of vertical slide valves back-to-back between the cylinders was getting very cramped.

No 9 and 10 had new 7ft 0in driving wheels instead of 7ft 8in, fitted in 1890. They lasted in service until 1905–1906. No 10 was the direct ancestor of the design which Dean at last introduced as his standard express engine, the 7ft 8in singles. The first 30 of these brought out in 1891–2 were 2–2–2s with double frames and underhung springs, so that they could be converted for use on the broad gauge if necessary. Although the broad gauge was to have only one more year of existence the shortage of engines had become so serious that the first eight of the class to be built, Nos 3021–28, were turned out as broad gauge engines. They ran in this form for about a year before being

Dean 4–2–2 7ft 8in single in standard gauge form as No 3034 *Behemoth* at Bath

converted to standard gauge. All 30 engines as 2–2–2s had 20in x 24in cylinders, the largest diameter ever used on single drivers anywhere. To feed them a larger boiler was necessary, but the diameter could not be increased because of the larger driving wheels. The barrel was therefore made unusually long at 11ft 6in, and a return was made to the raised round-top firebox as used by Gooch. Even so, the cylinders proved to be too big, and the diameter was soon reduced to 19in. The long boiler placed excessive weight on the leading wheels and caused the engines to be unsteady at the leading end. Matters came to a head in 1893 when No 3021 broke its leading axle and became derailed in Box Tunnel. Soon afterwards, all 30 engines were rebuilt with leading bogies, and between 1894 and 1899 fifty more were built new as 4–2–2s with 19in cylinders. In this final form Dean had at last produced a successful express engine, but only after several attempts after he had been in office for 15 years. Even so, it was probably a mistake to build so many at this late period.

The engines were magnificent runners with light trains. The feat of No 3065 in averaging 71mph from Bristol to Paddington on an Ocean Mail Special in 1904 is well known. Trains were already becoming too heavy for singles by the time the last batches were turned out in 1898–9. Ironically, it was the Great Western itself which had introduced the first vestibuled all-corridor train in 1892, for the London–Birkenhead service. This had been done under

Dean's authority, though one suspects that Churchward, then manager of the carriage works, was the driving force. The increasing use of corridor trains and then dining cars meant that the average weight of express trains soon doubled. By the time the last 7ft 8in singles were built it was becoming increasingly difficult to find suitable work for them, and all had a short life. The building of the first 30 was justified; to turn out 80 was a waste of money. They came too late.

By this time all five Scottish railways and most of the English main lines had plenty of admirable 4–4–0s as their principal express engines; only the Great Northern under the aged Patrick Stirling and the Great Western under Dean lagged behind.

In 1894 Dean had built four 4–4–0 express engines, the Armstrong class, nominally 'rebuilds' of Nos 7, 8, 14 and 16 already mentioned. They probably incorporated the 7ft driving wheels of their predecessors, but they were new engines, with the same boilers, cylinders and bogies as the singles. They should have been the answer. Unfortunately they were built with the over-large 20in cylinders and were not altered like the singles, so were not given a fair chance. They acquired an indifferent reputation, doubtless because of the cylinders over-taxing the boilers. One very good feature was that they were given frames of adequate depth, and never needed all the patching and welding that most subsequent 4–4–0s required.

In the next year the Dukes were introduced; they were so called because of the name given to the first of the class, No 3252 *Duke of Cornwall*. In their early days though they were often called Devons,

Duke class 4–4–0 No 3271 *Eddystone*, at Reading in 1924. It has a Belpaire boiler and top feed

because they were employed working passenger trains in Devon and Cornwall, which they usually took-over from the singles at Newton Abbot. It is questionable if the latter could have taken themselves over Dainton, Rattery and Hemerdon banks, let alone haul trains over them.

The Dukes were quite small engines, with 5ft 7in (later 5ft 8in) driving wheels, 18in x 26in cylinders, double frames and an 8ft 6in coupled wheelbase. The slide valves were again underneath the cylinders, driven directly by Stephenson gear. They were the ancestors of a very large family of locomotives which in 'Dukedog' form lasted until 1960. No 9017 survives in preservation on the Bluebell Railway in Sussex.

With larger boilers on the same frames, they became the very numerous and useful general purpose Bulldogs. The Atbaras, and Flowers were basically Bulldogs, with 6ft 8in driving wheels. The Cities were the same with larger boilers, Standard No 4 in place of Standard No 2, while the Aberdares were the 2–6–0 freight version. All these classes had the same design and dimensions for their cylinders and motion, so *Duke of Cornwall* was very much a pioneer.

In 1897 the twenty Badmintons appeared, and the Great Western at last had a sizeable class of express passenger 4–4–0s. Again, cylinders and motion were the same, but the coupled wheelbase was longer at 9ft 0in, the same as the Armstrongs. Coupled wheels were 6ft 8in, but the most significant feature was the Belpaire firebox, the first use of a pattern which was to become practically universal on the Great Western.

Drawings exist showing that the Badmintons were originally designed with round-top fireboxes. It appears that before they could be built Dean was beginning to retire into the background as his mental powers atrophied, and the change to Belpaire was instigated by Churchward. The last of the class to be built, *Waterford*, showed Churchward influence even more clearly, as it had the first of the Standard 2 boilers, parallel at this time, but domeless, with safety valves on the barrel, and a high Belpaire firebox.

This was the very first of the huge family of Churchward boilers, which in tapered form were fitted to all the larger Great Western engines, went with Stanier to the LMS, and used in modified form on some of the British Railways standard types. A boiler of much the

Badminton Class 4–4–0 No 3308 *Savernake* as built. Afterwards it was rebuilt with taper boiler and renumbered 4116

same dimensions had appeared a few months previously on *Bulldog*, but that had a dome, and the safety valves over the firebox in the usual place. This was the original Standard 2.

For all these 4–2–2s and 4–4–0s Dean had at last designed a bogie which would stay on the rails. In fact it stayed on remarkably well, for the risks taken with the Ocean Mail Specials a few years later were fearsome, yet no accident occurred. In particular the speeds maintained by *City of Truro* down the twists and turns of Rattery and Dainton banks must have been highly dangerous, and credit must be given to the Dean suspension bogie for the fact that there were no derailments.

This bogie was of unusual and ingenious design. It had to be, as the steam chest covers on all these engines were underneath. A normal centre pin casting would have made access to the valves impossible. Instead, four pillars were fixed to the inside frames, pointing downwards, two on each side between the bogie wheels. Each ended with a stout collar and a screw thread. A cross-member in the form of a casting fitted on these pillars and secured by nuts. It extended beyond the pillars, and at the ends was suspended from the bogie frame by hanger bolts, with cups containing rubber pads at each end. The bogie pin projected upwards into the bogie centre, entering it from below instead of above in the usual way. The bogie centre had some lateral sliding movement, controlled by springs. There was thus ample control, for the hangers had a certain amount of centring effect in the manner of a swing link bogie, which augmented the action of the side control springs.

Good features of these bogies were an adequate wheelbase, 7ft 0in on the 4–2–2s, Armstrongs and Badmintons, 6ft 6in on all the others, and wheels of a good size, varying from 3ft 7in to 4ft 1in, according to driving wheel size. Each wheel was individually sprung with plate springs of adequate length. To gain access to the valve chests, all that was necessary was to undo the four nuts, lift the front of the engine slightly with a crane, jacks or sheerlegs, and the bogie and cross-member could be run out as a unit. This proved an excellent bogie for the comparatively short engines for which it was used. It would probably not have done for longer engines such as 4–6–0s or 4–4–2s, as only very limited side movement or swivelling were possible before fouling the main outside frames. However, with the exception of No 36, known as the 'Crocodile', a one-off experimental 4–6–0 built by Dean in 1896, no long locomotive of this double-frame type was built.

Following the Badmintons, forty 4–4–0s generally similar to *Waterford* were built in 1900–01. These were the Atbaras, and in their design was incorporated what was a retrograde feature. Probably in the interests of standardisation the bogie, coupled and total wheelbases were all reduced to be the same as on the Dukes and Bulldogs. The coupled wheelbase was 8ft 6in compared with 9ft 0in on the Badmintons and Armstrongs. This had unfortunate ramifications later on, for this short coupled wheelbase was retained both on the Cities and the outside-cylinder County class 4–4–0s. Probably because of this short wheelbase the Class 4 boiler, first used on the Cities, was designed with 7ft firebox, the same as on the much smaller Class 2 boiler. This upset the proportions of the Class 4 boiler, giving it a small firebox and grate for the large barrel and tube heating surface. As a result, the Counties, the 43xx 2–6–0s, the 2–8–0 and 2–8–2 tank engines of later years were all liable to run short of steam if driven very hard. Had the 9ft 0in wheelbase been retained, the Class 4 boiler would probably have been given a rather longer firebox, with great benefit to its steaming qualities. It was a good boiler, but not so good size for size as the Class 2 or the Class 1.

There is some evidence that the Atbaras were designed with cheapness in mind. Not only was the wheelbase reduced as compared with the Badmintons, but the frames were straight-topped, instead of being raised over the driving horns to give extra strength where most needed. These straight-topped frames gave endless trouble in years to come, needing much welding and patching to deal with cracks in the region of the horn gaps. The same applied to Churchward's outside-cylinder engines, which also had straight-topped frames and similar weakness. The curved frames of the Badmintons gave some trouble, but not so much, even when fitted for a time with the heavier Class 4 boilers. If cheaper construction had been the object, it would seem to have been better to discard the heavier and more expensive double frames, and to use normal inside frames as on the very successful Dean Goods.

The short coupled wheelbase evidently used on the Counties in the interest of standardisation was particularly bad in their case, as in conjunction with outside cylinders and 30in stroke it led to much rolling and rough riding. Most 4–4–0s of comparable size and power on other railways had a coupled wheelbase of 9ft 6in or more.

Two quite admirable fittings came into use during Dean's reign. One was the special Great Western form of vacuum brake, much the best in this country, and possibly in the world. It was devised by 'Young Joe' Armstrong, son of the former locomotive superintendent, with the assistance of the then young Churchward on Dean's instructions. Its special features were 25in of vacuum instead of the usual 20in or 21in, maintained by a crosshead-driven pump instead of a small ejector. It was more economical in steam, and had the great advantage that if the engine was steaming badly and the pressure became low, the brakes did not add to the problem by leaking on, as they were liable to do with dependence on an ejector. The very neat and compact backhead fitting, comprising application valves for steam brake on the engine and vacuum on the train with the ejector and its steam valve all in one, remained in use on the smaller engines right until the end of steam. Churchward added direct-admission valves to the coaches and vans in about 1903, (the LNER was experimenting with such things in 1938 when *Mallard* broke the world speed record for steam traction) and then it was a very good brake.

I have been on Swindon station and have watched milk trains arrive, composed entirely of 6-wheel vans with brakes on only four of the six wheels — yet they would charge into the station and stop like a London Transport District Line train at St James's Park. I have also been a passenger in trains checked at 70mph or more, which were able to stop very quickly and quite smoothly. By comparison, the Midland version of the vacuum brake, adopted by the LMS and then by British Rail, was a very feeble affair. Readers may remember that when the LMS tried to break the speed record with the Coronation in 1937 it had great difficulty in slowing-down and narrowly escaped a pile-up in Crewe station.

The other excellent device was the screw reverse, first used on the 7ft 8in singles and the Armstrong 4–4–0s. This was simple and straightforward, quick-acting, with only about eight turns from full foreward to full reverse gear. I never saw one that was hard to turn, in spite of the quick-thread screw. It permitted very fine adjustment of cut-off, and had an excellent looking device. The notched wheel was fixed to the stand, and the catchbolt slid inside one arm of the handle, being worked by one of the hand grips which was pivoted. It gave a more rigid lock than the type where the notched wheel revolved, and the catch was pivoted on the stand. Stanier took it to the LMS where it was equally successful, and much better liked than the BR standard 'mangle wheel' with bevel gears, which was slow, cumbersome and awkward.

As we shall see, the strange thing is that it was much less used on the GWR than it might have been. Initially a steam reverser was used on Atbaras, Cities, 2–4–2 tanks, Aberdare 2–6–0s and many Bulldogs. Then a lever reverser was adopted for all Churchward's freight, tank, and mixed-traffic engines, and even on the earlier 29xx 4–6–0s and County class 4–4–0s, for which it was most unsuitable.

While on the subject of fittings, a little must be said about safety valves, as there is a considerable risk of a fallacy passing into history. This concerns the type of safety valve carried by GWR locomotives. It has been said that they were Ramsbottom valves, and to the extent that they released steam gently just below maximum boiler pressure, rather than suddenly exploding into life at the critical point — the 'all or nothing' characteristic of the pop safety valve — they followed the Ramsbottom pattern. But, as can be seen in the accompanying diagram, that was where the resemblance ended.

A tremendous amount has been written and published about Great Western engines, and I have waded through all I can find. Unfortunately most writers have quite a lot to say about safety valve 'bonnets' from the Gooch 'squashed bonnet box' as Hamilton Ellis called it, to the 'milk churn' shape used since Dean's day. They discuss which engines had the shorter type and which did not, but say nothing about the valves inside. Having studied photographs and drawings of almost every type of Great Western engine ever built, I have only found one which certainly had Ramsbottom valves. This was *Waterford*, the odd one out among the Badminton 4–4–0s, being the only one built with a domeless boiler. It did not keep the Ramsbottom valves for long. Another probability is the original Kruger, No 2601, but photographic evidence is not conclusive.

Ramsbottom safety valves had one tension spring shared by two valves, the three all connected by a 'cowtail' lever. All Great Western engines from 1900 onwards were built with two simple direct-loaded safety valves with compression springs, the very opposite of the Ramsbottom arrangement. The two valves were quite independent of each other, again in contrast to the Ramsbottom.

The Great Western system was an excellent one. Ramsbottom valves were known to stick sometimes, occasionally causing boiler explosions and deaths. The 'pop' valves used on all other British railways from about 1912–20 onwards ought to have been forbidden under the Noise Abatement Acts! They made an appalling row, starting on full bore so suddenly that they could give both people and animals a bad shock. They were 'all or nothing', blowing-off furiously or shutting-off suddenly and completely. Once lifted, they seldom closed until some 10lb or 15lb pressure had been lost. By contrast, the Great Western valves could be and very often were kept just 'sizzling', maintaining the designed pressure without waste of steam.

This seems a good place to round off the subject. In the early days of Gooch, nearly all engines had two Salter spring-balance safety valves, as did most engines on other lines at the time. Later on, the usual arrangement under the Armstrongs and Dean was to have one Salter valve on the left, sharing the same casing with a direct-loaded valve on the right. The Salter lever was long, and emerged diagonally through a slot in the casing, then entered the cab through another slot, well over towards the left side. In footplate views of a Duke, a 7ft 8in single, and the crocodile, the large casing of the Salter spring is a very prominent feature inside the cab, and attached to the boiler backhead on the left-hand side.

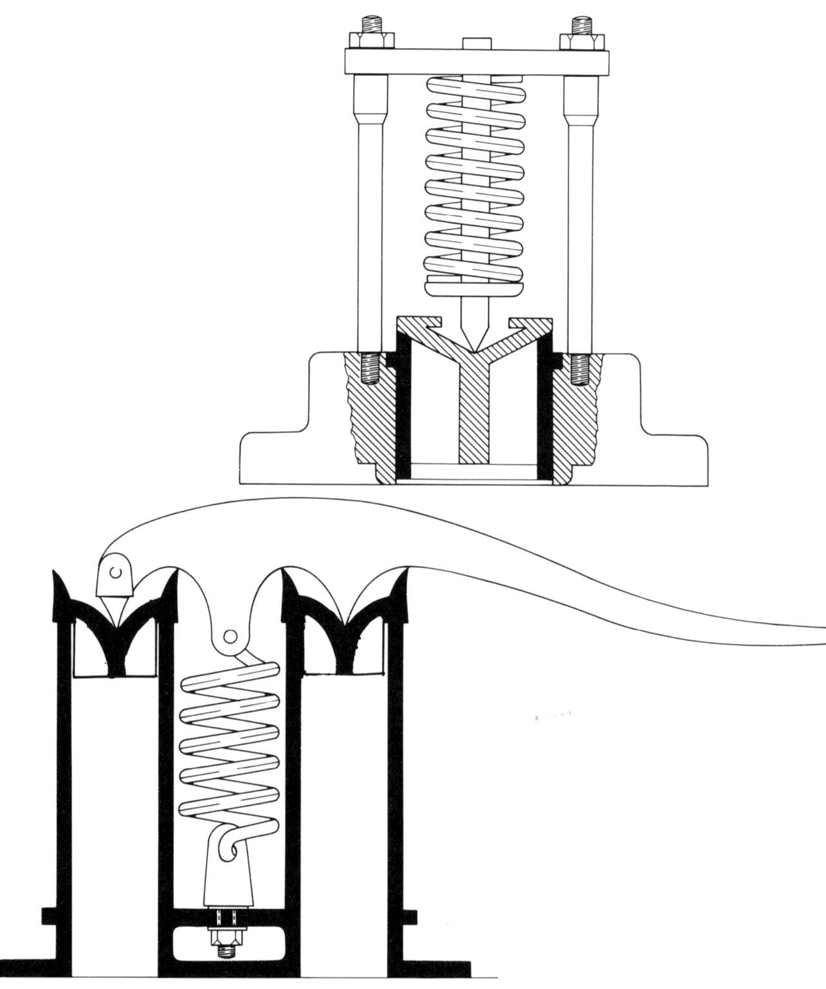

The Ramsbottom safety valve (below) contrasted with the Swindon direct loaded type (above), used in pairs within a conical brass casing in all twentieth century GW locomotives. (*Author, courtesy Allen & Unwin*)

5
A Transitional Period

As we have already noted, Dean's mental powers began to fail from about 1897 onwards. Until 1902, when he was formally appointed locomotive, carriage and wagon superintendent, Churchward was for all practical purposes in charge of the department, although Dean continued in office as a kind of figurehead. The board showed great consideration for Dean, and Churchward evidently exercised much tact during this difficult period.

From Churchward's point of view this interim arrangement had one great advantage. It enabled him to make his early experiments and learn by his mistakes before he was officially in charge, which was good for his reputation. Once appointed to the top job he could go right ahead with his scheme for standard classes, of what were then quite revolutionary designs, with more or less instant success.

Mistakes there certainly were. The early Belpaire fireboxes, very square with flat sides and tops and sharp angles, were far from trouble-free. Cracks tended to appear, at the front around the throat-plate in particular. The large boiler of this type, with parallel barrel and square outer firebox, fitted to the first large-wheeled 4–6–0 No 100 *William Dean*, was particularly troublesome. Churchward was very quick to learn from these faults, and soon developed his own form of Belpaire firebox, with no extensive flat surfaces, but easy curves everywhere. The firebox was tapered down from front to rear, and the barrel from back to front, giving ample space for circulation of water and release of steam where it was most needed, around the firebox tubeplate.

This type of boiler proved remarkably successful throughout the life of GWR and later Western Region steam. It was equally successful on the LMS from 1932 onwards, and later on the British Rail standard locomotives. Though more expensive in first cost, it proved to have a much longer life and to be cheaper in maintenance than other types. It solved the problem of using higher pressures without

Aberdare 2–6–0 goods engine No 2602, as running about 1915 with superheater and top feed

incurring excessive boiler maintenance costs. On other railways, the fear of such expense inhibited the use of anything more than 180lb/sq in for many years, and led to the misguided practice of reducing pressure on superheated engines. For example, when Ivatt on the Great Northern produced a superheated version of his large Atlantics, he reduced the boiler pressure from 175lb/sq in to 150lb/sq in, and the engines not surprisingly proved rather sluggish. Gresley soon compromised on these and the other Atlantics when they were superheated, with a boiler pressure of 170lb/sq in.

There was one rather disastrous experimental design produced during this period, the 'Kruger' family. A fitting epitaph on these engines might well be 'ugly is as ugly does'. For generations which have lived through one or even two world wars, it is hard to realise what a deep impression the Boer War in far away South Africa made on the people of this country when it took place in 1899–1902. After nearly 100 years of seemingly effortless British supremacy, this local but difficult struggle came as a great shock. A number of crack Great Western express 4–4–0s of 1900–01, the Atbaras, were named after people, places or warships connected with the Boer War. Paul Kruger, the Boer leader and President of the Transvaal, became a bogey man, just as Napoleon had a hundred years before, and the Kaiser and Hitler were to be later on. Hence the nicknames bestowed on the monstrosities we are about to describe, 'Kruger' and 'Mrs Kruger'.

At this time there was a pressing need for more powerful engines for main line goods service, especially the heavy South Wales coal traffic through the Severn Tunnel. The quite excellent Armstrong and Dean 0–6–0s were very small, and showed no real increase in power since the 1860s. Dean had had one try in 1895 with the 'Crocodile', a 4–6–0 which was more-or-less an elongated Duke with 4ft 7in driving wheels, and what was really a broad gauge style of firebox. This was of the round raised-top pattern, wider than the boiler barrel, and with straight sides continued down to a 5ft 6in wide grate. This last feature was only feasible on a small-wheeled engine, and was made possible in this case by cutting the inside frames short in front of the firebox, and relying entirely on the outside frames for the rear part of the engine. No 36 provided an adequate increase of power, but the design was not followed up, and the engine had a short life of only nine years, with a mileage of 171,000. There seems to be no record of serious trouble with this engine. It may well have been the decline of William Dean which led to the design not being developed.

Churchward, by now in charge in fact though not in name, had

4–6–0 goods engine No 2601, nicknamed 'Kruger'. Note the combustion chamber, the sandbox straddling boiler, and the coil springs for coupled wheels

4–4–0 No 3437 *City of Gloucester* as built. These locomotives had larger boilers than the Atbara 4–4–0s. Later it was numbered 3714

another try with 4–6–0 No 2601, nicknamed 'Kruger', turned out into traffic in the last month of the century, December 1899. This engine was of much the same length as No 36, though the distribution of the wheelbase was different. A similar frame arrangement allowed a wide firebox. Otherwise the engine was entirely different, with many experimental features — too many novelties at once it would seem. The wide firebox was in this case of raised Belpaire type, with a combustion chamber no less than 3ft 6in long. There was no dome, and the safety valves were on the barrel in the usual Churchward style. The coupled wheels had a strange mixture of coil and volute springs, in nests above the footplating. The bogie was unique, basically of Dean pattern, but with inside frames, swing links outside, and a rather short wheelbase, 5ft 6in. Piston valves were fitted above the cylinders, driven from the Stephenson gear through rocking levers. This again was unique on the GWR for inside cylinder-engines, where the usual practice was to have valves underneath, driven directly by inclined valve motion. Single slide bars were used, and the long stroke, for an inside-cylinder engine, of 28in. The sandbox took the form of a large saddle over the front of the boiler, making the already stumpy-looking barrel appear even shorter. The boiler was pitched very high at 8ft 9in, the cab towered over the low tender, and the appearance of the engine was so odd that the nickname bestowed by the men was quite understandable.

A very similar engine, No 2602, followed in 1901, differing in having a pony truck in place of the bogie, and plate springs in place of coils for the leading coupled axle only. This engine naturally became 'Mrs Kruger', but when eight more followed in 1903 one can only assume that Paul Kruger was a polygamist with a sizeable harem! These eight were slightly more presentable in that the saddle type sandbox was omitted.

These engines were a dismal failure, and had very short lives, varying from three to six years, with mileages of from 30,000 to 60,000; in the case of No 2602 the mileage was 80,000. Almost all the experimental features gave trouble, especially the combustion chambers, although the boiler pressure was reduced from 200lb/sq in to 180lb/sq in and then to 165lb/sq in. The 28in stroke disagreed with the crank axles, which had very short lives. It would seem that the heavy and lopsided crossheads necessitated by the single slide bars caused piston rods to bend, for afterwards Churchward always insisted that 'crossheads must be symmetrical', and from that time used nothing but the two-bar 'alligator' pattern. The steep 1 in 7 slope of the cylinders seems to have been disadvantageous, for in all his subsequent designs Churchward insisted on cylinders being perfectly horizontal, even when this meant raising them above the centre line of the axles by as much as 2½ inches.

Although the Krugers were so unsuccessful, they were of great importance in the development of locomotive design at Swindon. They taught Churchward very clearly that 'you cannot put new wine into old wine skins'. If engines were to be introduced of far higher efficiency than had been obtained up to that time, incorporating long stroke, long valve travel, small piston clearance, and high boiler pressure, a new basic lay-out was essential. The Victorian inside-cylinder concept just had to go, and Churchward turned to the American outside-cylinder type for his newly planned series of standard locomotives.

The British addiction to using inside cylinders practically exclusively, which coincided almost exactly with the reign of Queen Victoria before it began to decline, can now be seen as a very curious phenomenon. The *Rocket* and its near sisters had followed the logical arrangement of outside cylinders driving directly on to crankpins in the wheels. This eliminated the need for expensive and troublesome crank-axles, and of course provided much better accessibility to the motion. Yet within about five or six years from the building of *Rocket*, most British engineers changed over to inside cylinders.

By the 1880s the only British designers using outside cylinders were David Jones on the Highland, William Adams on the North London and then the London & South Western, and Patrick Stirling on the Great Northern for one class only. Even Adams soon abandoned outside cylinders for all except his main line express passenger locomotives. Only David Jones stayed faithful to the more sensible arrangement, and proved to be right. In this and in the pioneering of the 4–6–0 he was the father of the mainstream of British 20th century design. The Victorian type of engine with inside cylinders proved to be a blind alley in the long-term development of the steam locomotive. It was mainly confined to the British Isles, and a few countries which had British locomotive engineers, such as India and Egypt, and places like Holland which had imported many engines from such British firms as Beyer Peacock, and Sharp Stewart. The rest of the world, North America in particular, always adhered almost entirely to outside-cylinder designs.

This strange changeover by most British designers around the 1830s seems to have been something of a panic measure, due to the tendency of the light short-wheelbase engines of the period to yawing from side to side from the motion of outside pistons, which became alarming as speeds increased. The Americans dealt with this problem much more sensibly by adopting bogies from the start.

Around the turn of the century several British designers, Ivatt on the Great Northern, Worsdell on the North Eastern, and three or four years later Robinson on the Great Central and Manson on the Glasgow & South Western did go over to outside cylinders, but only for their very largest engines. Their main output continued to be in the Victorian manner, with some increase in size and power. It was on the Great Western, which had been exclusively an inside-cylinder line from the start, with the exception of Gooch's few ill-starred Metropolitan tanks, that the real breakthrough occurred. From the time Churchward took office in 1902, all new designs for the next 20 years had outside cylinders. A few double-framed inside-cylinder engines such as Cities and Bulldogs were built, but these were stop-gaps — Dean designs with improved (and in some cases larger) boilers, to hold the fort until the new range could be completed.

6

Churchward's Great Work

We now come to the reign of George Jackson Churchward, as locomotive, carriage and wagon superintendent. (He was entitled chief mechanical engineer only from 1916 onwards.)

There can be little doubt that he was by far the greatest designer of locomotives who has ever held high office on the railways of Great Britain. His locomotives and coaches really were to his design. The stamp both of his genius, and his preferences — we can even say prejudices — was noticeable in almost every detail. In this he was very different from men like Sir Henry Fowler and R. E. L. Maunsell, who were mainly administrators, and left the direction of design largely to their chief draughtsmen and technical assistants. Harold Holcroft has described how Churchward had a habit of visiting the board of an individual draughtsman, sitting on his stool, and holding a conference with the chief draughtsman, the leading draughtsman, the individual draughtsman and sometimes representatives from the works and the running department. In this way he kept a close personal eye not only on the broad tendencies of design, but on the details as well, and he himself decided the next step after such consultations.

On the other hand, he was good at picking out promising young men to whom he could and did delegate experimental work, detailed design and new projects, but always his was the guiding hand, and he had the final say as to what was done and how it was done.

In the last half of the nineteenth century it had been very unusual for a standard class of new locomotive to be designed from basic principles. Most design was very much 'rule of thumb', not really thought out afresh but based on 'what we've always done . . .' Design had got into a groove. Many designers who had done well with small engines of conventional Victorian type ran into all kinds of trouble when they sought to provide greatly increased power to cope with the much greater twentieth century loads. Notable examples were on the

4–4–2 No 189 *Talisman*, at Bristol, Temple Meads. It was rebuilt as a 4–6–0 and numbered 2989 in 1912

London & South Western, the Lancashire & Yorkshire, and the Caledonian, where the various 4–6–0s were not nearly so successful as the 4–4–0s had been.

Helped probably by his experience with the Krugers, as related in the last chapter, Churchward was very quick to realise that it was no good trying to enlarge the conventional British inside-cylinder locomotive. A new start was essential.

Influenced no doubt by his personal friendship with A. W. Gibbs of the Pennsylvania Railroad in the USA, Churchward took a close look at North American practice, and saw in this a basis for the new direction he was seeking. There, simple, rugged accessible designs with outside cylinders had long been usual, and by the turn of the century the 4–6–0 was becoming well established for passenger and fast freight, the natural successor to the standard American 4–4–0. It is true that a few years later in America 4–6–0s were largely superseded by 4–6–2s and eventually 4–8–4s, but that in no way invalidates what we have been saying. It did not happen until after Churchward had completed his plans for a standard range of locomotives.

Churchward's scheme for a new range of engines, to provide for all main line requirements for the next 20 years and beyond, was worked out and put on paper in 1901, the year before he actually became superintendent. He was therefore ready to build the first prototypes almost at once, which then could be tested thoroughly before being reproduced in quantity.

A whole range of standard components was designed first. Outside cylinders of one size only, 18in diameter by 30 in stroke, incorporated steam chests of ample size for 10in piston valves. These were combined with the steam chests and half the smokebox saddle, a regular American practice. As Churchward insisted on cylinders being horizontal, the left- and right-hand castings could be and were interchangeable, making appreciable savings in the pattern shop and foundry. When the two castings were bolted together on the centre line, a very rigid structure resulted, with no joints subject to steam pressure, except of course the entries of the steam pipes. The cylindrical smokeboxes were very substantial, rolled from ½in plate. They were bolted to the saddle, a rigid support for the boiler was provided, and there was little likelihood of the smokebox drawing air and killing the draught, even after long and hard service. With the light wrapper type smokeboxes used elsewhere, this was a great source of trouble as mileage mounted.

Axleboxes and motion were to be standard throughout the range. The axleboxes were of ample dimensions, with large bearing areas, and very rigid. They were of cast-steel with pressed-in brasses and a thin white metal lining, with the surface unbroken by oil grooves or anything else. Large keeps allowed room for an easily removable oil tray, containing a large pad pressed up under the axle by springs. Top oil was introduced at the sides immediately below the white metal, and was carried up into the bearing by the rotation of the axle. A collar of worsted sealing the inside of the bearing kept the oil in, grit and dirt out. These were probably the best plain axleboxes ever devised. They made it possible for engines to be driven hard and fast for hours on end without running hot. When taken to the LMS by Stanier 30 years later, this type almost eliminated the hot boxes which had been prevalent there, and which seem to have been regarded until than as an 'act of God' which had to be endured.

The motion parts were standard throughout the range. One pattern of crosshead and slidebars sufficed for all. There were two lengths of connnecting rod of the same pattern, two lengths of extension rod, valve rod and eccentric rod — other parts were the same.

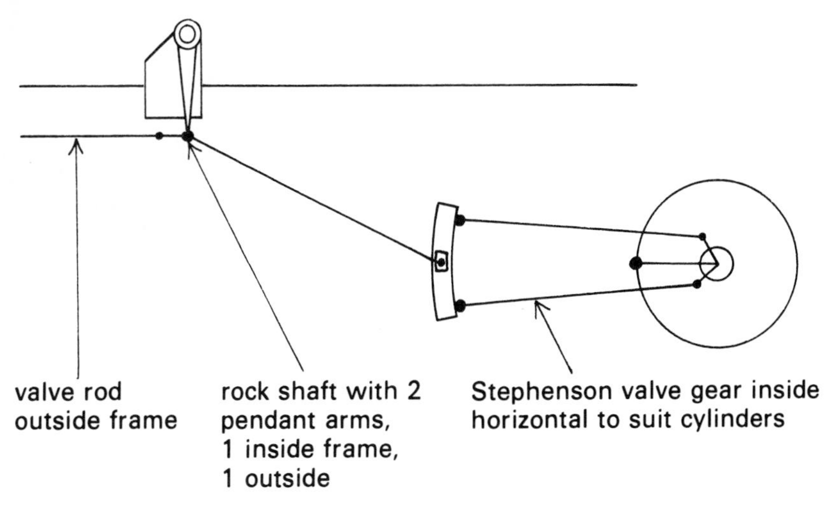

GWR version of Stephenson valve gear as used on all the standard outside cylinder locomotives

One pattern and length of coupling rod served all the six-coupled engines, another all the four-coupled. The connecting rods of H-section and ample strength were of very simple design. Churchward pioneered the plain circular bushed big-end, which was very widely copied later on. Up to that time split big-ends had been universal, either of the marine type, or otherwise complicated and heavy forms involving cotters, or sometimes screw controlled wedges.

Marine big-ends, for some reason I have never been able to ascertain, seem to have given a lot of trouble with heating. The various cottered varieties usually gave good service, but their weight was undesirable in a rapidly-moving part, and their assembly and adjustment needed considerable care from a skilled fitter. Plain bushed ends had been very widely used on coupling rods for many years. Applied to connecting rods, they were simpler, lighter, stronger and cheaper than any form of split bearing. There was nothing to get out of adjustment or come apart in service, which could be disastrous. There have been instances of split big-ends coming to pieces after running hot. The least serious consequence would be the end of the cylinder knocked out and the piston smashed. At the worst, the boiler could be penetrated and explode, or the engine be derailed by the flying rod, or both. Given the necessary tooling, it was a simple and quick process to press out a worn bush and press in a new one.

In this connection an amusing story is told of the LMS in the 1930s. Sir Harold Hartley, vice-president for scientific and engineering matters, had established a kind of 'think tank', a research department quite separate from any of the works, and not under the control of the chief mechanical engineer. It was not really surprising that its ideas and suggestions were often quite impractical. One of the bright young 'boffins' in this set-up was heard to enquire '. . . if solid big-ends are so satisfactory with outside cylinders, why are they not used inside as well?' I am sure that readers will know the answer to that one without any prompting!

Piston valves and pistons were common to the whole range, 10in and 18in diameter respectively. The pistons were of cast-iron of a hollow box section, with flat faces. The piston rods were screwed in with a measured torque, pinned and turned-off flush, so that simple flat cylinder covers could be used. This, in conjunction with the non-adjustable big-ends, horizontal cylinders and very accurate assembly, made possible a smaller piston clearance than anyone else dared to use. This was important for economy in steam, as the amount needed to fill the clearance volume at each stroke reduces the expansion ratio. The clearance volume was further reduced by making the steam ports very short, and quite straight. This was achieved by making the steamchests rather longer than the cylinders, so that the piston valve heads were above the ends of the cylinders in mid-position. Most other designers of the period threw away some of the advantages of piston valves by keeping close to the slide valve proportions, setting the valve heads close together near the middle of the cylinder length and so being forced to use the long and tortuous ports necessary with slide valves.

The design of the Stephenson valve gear was unusual. It is a feature of this gear that if it is properly arranged the lead increases as the gear is notched-up, and the cut-off shortened. This had been considered a disadvantage, as it could bring about excessive lead, causing knocking at short cut-offs. Much was made in the technical press of the period of the virtue of constant lead when Joy or Walschaert valve gear was used. Churchward however made a virtue of this variable lead. By deliberately using short eccentric rods he actually increased the variation. Arranging for a negative lead in full gear, he

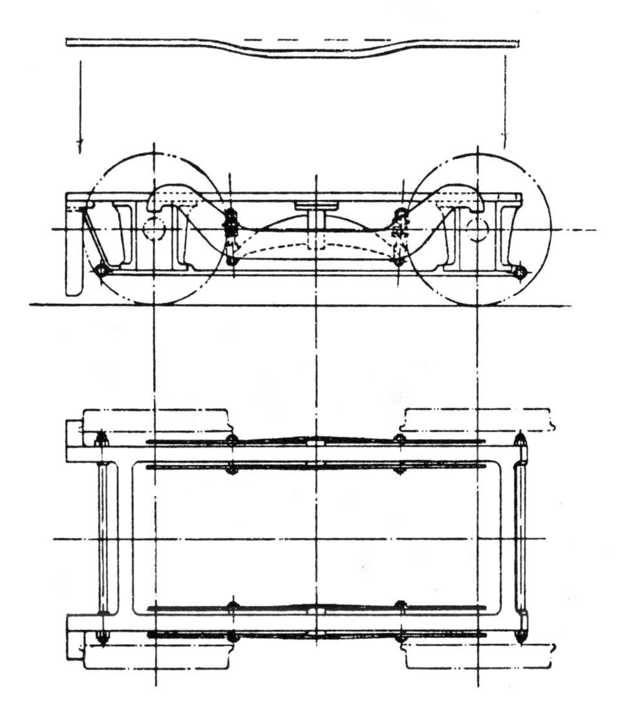

Bar frame bogie, showing at top how frame could be bent upwards when spring weakened

ensured that at the normal running cut-offs of 22 to 28 percent, the lead was just right for high speed. It allowed for rapid filling of the cylinder with steam at the beginning of the stroke, and adequate cushioning of the piston at the end of the stroke. He thus made the best of both worlds. As we saw earlier, Harold Holcroft has pointed out that this proper use of variable lead was rather analogous to advancing the spark as engine speed increases in a motor vehicle. The same lead at all cut-offs is in fact a disadantage. Lead is a hindrance in starting and slow pulling.

Henry Ivatt of the Great Northern, having built some 0–8–2 tank engines to provide quicker acceleration on the London suburban trains, found they were so reluctant to run fast that they had to be relegated to coal traffic in the East Midlands. He complained of the impossibility of combining the attributes of the 'drayhorse and the racehorse', the 0–8–2 tank's pulling power and the free-running of

4–6–0 No 2909 *Lady of Provence*, an early Saint with angular footplating and lever reverse

the single-driver. Churchward solved the problem with his version of Stephenson valve gear.

His masterpiece, the 2-cylinder 4–6–0 Saint class, became famous for both speed and hard pulling. Many drivers considered them faster than the 4-cylinder Stars though in the absence of speedometers they may have been misled by the rougher riding. They were unquestionably not only fast but capable of hauling very heavy trains at high speed over long distances. They exceeded Churchward's published target 'two tons drawbar pull at 70mph, on the level' by a considerable amount. On the other hand they were remarkably good at starting from rest and slow pulling with heavy loads on long and steep gradients. O. S. Nock has established that on the long climbs between Newport and Hereford, with trains of between 450 and 500 tons, they not only did better than the Stars with the same boiler, but were unequalled by the larger Castles, with 17% more tractive effort. Mr Nock also details a run on the High Wycombe route to Birmingham, when No 2906 *Lady of Lynn* showed that this remarkable capacity for hard work uphill was still available at 60mph to 64mph. Churchward had achieved what Ivatt had thought impossible — he succeeded in combining the drayhorse and the racehorse in one engine.

With this excellent valve gear, Churchward used a long lap to the valves, 1⅝in instead of the average at that time of 1in or less, and a long valve travel, 6¼in against the usual 4in or thereabouts. These two features gave a full port opening to exhaust, and a reasonable opening for admission, even when well linked up to 20 percent to 25 percent cut-off. These apparently very small changes in dimensions, together with the large piston valves and wide direct ports, made all the difference. The adequate port openings not only gave free running but power at speed, while the ability to run on short cut-offs allowed notable economy in coal.

Three sizes of driving and coupled wheel were standardised to cover all duties; a commonsense and economical decision, which Churchward's successors notably failed to carry on, as we shall see. The sizes were 4ft 7½in for goods and mineral engines, 5ft 8in for mixed-traffic, and 6ft 8½in for express passenger locomotives. Instead of the then usual crescent-shaped balance weights in one with the cast-steel wheel centre, the wheels were plain, and had balance weights with square ends, formed of two steel plates riveted together through the spokes, and with a lead filling cast into the space between. This enabled the weights to be adjusted to very close limits, after running each pair of wheels on a special balancing machine which was installed at Swindon Works.

The 1901 scheme envisaged six locomotive types only to cover all the heavier duties. The cornerstone was the express 4–6–0 which in due course materialised in the 29xx or Saint class. Another 4–6–0, with 5ft 8in wheels, was drawn out for mixed traffic, and more particularly to replace the Dukes and Bulldogs on passenger trains west of Newton Abbot. Such engines were not built in Churchward's time, but the Granges of 1936–39 were just such a design. So really were the Halls of 1928 onwards, with the slight difference of 6ft 0in coupled wheels. The 4–6–0, with one pair less of coupled wheels and a shorter boiler barrel and firebox, became the first County, a very powerful 4–4–0. The Counties' performance was however subject to the limitations of a small grate area and lack of reserve boiler power. This meant that their best performance depended more than usual on the skill, dedication, and co-operation of driver and fireman. If the driver was too heavy-handed by opening-out too much and for too long, if the fireman was not sufficiently skilful and painstaking, or the coal was of poor quality, then the Counties were more likely to run short of steam than the 4–6–0s. These had a much bigger boiler and firebox in relation to their tractive effort. The Counties' best work tended to be on undulating routes, or on trains making a number of stops. Downhill stretches or waiting in stations gave a chance for the boiler pressure to recover. The speeds they attained depended very much on the courage and endurance of the crew, since with their very short fixed wheelbase, large outside cylinders, and long stroke, they were notoriously rough riders.

The corresponding tank engine, a 4–4–2T for fast short-distance traffic, had a boiler of smaller diameter to keep down the weight, as did the 2–6–2 tank designed for mixed traffic and piloting heavy trains over steep gradients. Finally, there was to be the quite excellent 2–8–0, with the 4–6–0 boiler, for heavy freight. All but one of these types, the 5ft 8in 4–6–0 mentioned above, were soon built.

As soon as he was officially in charge, Churchward built several experimental prototypes, three of the large-wheeled 4–6–0, one 2–6–2 tank, and one 2–8–0. The 4–6–0 was the foundation of the range, and No 100, afterwards 2900 *William Dean*, was completed before Dean officially retired. The design however was pure Churchward. This engine was not very successful. I have already mentioned the troubles with the parallel boiler and square Belpaire firebox in the previous chapter, and the improvements which had to be made. The cylinders were different in No 100 from the later standard pattern. The valves were over the frames, and were operated by the normal type of rocking lever, which reverses the direction of movement. These valves were double-ported, only 6½in diameter. Enlarged to 7in then to 7½in, the most the design would allow, they still proved too small.

The next prototype, No 98, later 2998 *Ernest Cunard*, was the real pioneer of the standard classes. In this the taper boiler with the carefully shaped and curved firebox appeared. The cylinder design was different, with much larger piston valves, 10in diameter, almost immediately above the cylinders. The rockers driving the valves had two pendant arms, so that they only transferred the movement from inside the frames to outside without reversing its direction. A third experimental 4–6–0 soon followed, No 171 *Albion*, differing from No 98 only in the boiler pressure, which was 225lb/sq in instead of 200lb/sq in. With the building of *Albion* the definitive Churchward locomotive had arrived, and it is difficult to exaggerate its importance or its success. With the addition of superheating only about three years later, the standard general-purpose and passenger engine, which was to see out the end of steam on all major railways in the country, had been pioneered.

For the last 24 years of steam, the typical British passenger and mixed-traffic engine was a 4–6–0 with two outside cylinders and a high boiler steam pressure, 200lb/sq in to 225lb/sq in, large piston valves with ample sized short and direct ports, long lap and long valve travel. The Southern produced an engine of this type with the King Arthurs of 1925. The LMS had to wait till it had a chief mechanical engineer from Swindon, W. A. Stanier, before following suit with the 'Black Fives' of 1934. The LNER did not produce such a design until the B1 class of Edward Thompson's reign in 1942. The Great Western got there in 1903, or with the superheater in 1906, twenty years before anyone else. No wonder E. C. Poultney in his book *British Express Locomotive Development*, called the Saints 'the keystone of the arch'. Nos 98 and 171 were the biggest single step forward in design since Stephenson's *Rocket*.

The first 2–8–0, built in 1903 as No 97, was just as big an advance. No better or more powerful goods engine was produced for 50 years, until the BR Class 9 2–10–0s appeared. Stanier's Class 8 2–8–0s, built 32 years later, were slightly less powerful in tractive effort and

Churchward 2–8–0 No 2814. An early example as modified in 1911, with superheater, top feed, and curved drop-end footplating, but still with inside steampipes

No 3113, a large 2–6–2 tank as built in 1905. It was an early example of a very large family of locomotives. Note the straight back bunker

adhesion weight, and their Walschaert valve gear was as we have seen, not so well adapted to hard slow pulling. A Saint with driving wheels reduced to 6ft 0in, the Hall class, eventually numbered 330 engines, and was built right up to 1950. They were the inspiration for the famous Stanier 'Black Fives', of which over 800 were built, and the very similar BR Class 5 4–6–0s.

No 33, the original 2–6–2 tank of 1903, had about 300 successors of the same basic design. They continued to be built until well after Nationalisation, the last not until December 1949. There were several variations, Nos 3150 to 3190 had the larger Standard 4 boiler, and Nos 6100 to 6169, specially built for the London suburban services, had the smaller boiler pressed to 225lb/sq in, instead of 200lb/sq in. A few were also rebuilt around 1938 with non-standard size wheels, but called new engines. This was part of Collett's 'jiggery pokery', which we shall discuss later. The basic design was obviously most satisfactory, for it met all needs for nearly 60 years. Nothing as good was produced elsewhere until the first LMS 2–6–4 tanks of 1927 onwards, and these last were hardly as reliable. They seem to have been plagued with injector trouble and leaking water tanks.

We saw in the last chapter how the earlier Churchward boilers, with square Belpaire fireboxes and parallel barrels, gave trouble with cracking. Experiments carried out by Messrs Pearson and Cross, Churchward's trouble shooters, showed that circulation of the water was not very good. As we have seen, these troubles were completely overcome by tapering the boiler one way and the firebox the other, so that there was ample clearance round the firebox tubeplate for the water to circulate. The cracking of firebox plates was dealt with by making things flexible. The inner and outer boxes, instead of being square with flat sides, were curved to an adequate radius, and no stays were fitted close to the angles. As Churchward put it, 'the plates must be allowed to breathe'.

The abolition of the dome for large boilers was sound. As boilers grew larger, domes had to be so shallow that they were of very little use for enlarging the steam space, and ensuring dry steam at the regulator. Where used, they became little more than raised manhole covers. By insisting on a minimum of 2ft 0in between the crown of the inner firebox and the wrapper, Churchward found that there was drier steam and less priming than with a dome. With small boilers it was different. Domeless boilers were tried on the last batches of Wolverhampton saddle tanks, also on replacement boilers for Barnum 2–4–0s and some of the single drivers in the early 1900s. They were soon given up, and Churchward reverted to the very large domes of the late Dean period. Domes are useful when there is room to make them big.

For the larger boilers, the absence of a dome made it convenient to place the safety valves near the middle of the total boiler length, a much better place than at one end, particularly over the firebox where the most ebullition takes place. Furthermore, at the middle the water level is not much affected by change of gradient. For both reasons, blowing-off of water with the steam is less likely to occur. It is noticeable that such late designs as the Bulleid Pacifics and the

A Saint in final form, No 2945 *Hillingdon Court*, built with superheater and top feed. It is seen here at Bath Road in 1951 as fitted with outside steampipes in 1938. (*A. R. Brown*)

larger British Rail Standard locomotives had the safety valves near the middle of the boiler length, even though they did have manhole covers masquerading as domes.

Having developed a really satisfactory design of boiler remarkably quickly with great efficiency and decisiveness, a standard range was soon established, requiring only two sizes of flanging plates. Diameters were 5ft 6in tapering to 4ft 10in, and 5ft 0in tapering to 4ft 5in. Barrels were 14ft 9in or 11ft 0in long. Firebox length was 9ft 0in, giving a grate area of 27sq ft, and 7ft 0in with 20½sq ft of grate. The Standard No 1 boiler, used on 4–6–0s, 4–4–2s, and 2–8–0s, had all the larger dimensions. The Standard No 4 boiler first used on Cities, then Aberdares and Counties, and some years later on some 2–6–2 tanks, the 43xx 2–6–0s and the 2–8–0 tanks, had the shorter length and the larger diameter. The Standard No 2 boiler had the shorter length and the larger diameter. It became very widely used, being fitted to most of the inside-cylinder 4–4–0s, the 4–4–2 tanks, and the majority of the 2–6–2 tanks. A slight variant was the Standard 3 boiler. It was simply the No 2 with the barrel shortened by nine inches, to fit the 2–4–2 tanks. It was also used on some of the 3521 class, the curious Dean efforts which started as 0–4–2 tanks and finished up as 4–4–0 tender engines. Similar boilers but considerably smaller were designed for the 2–6–2 tank engines of the 44xx and 45xx classes, and the solitary small 4–4–2 tank No 4600. These were the Standard No 5.

In this way a range of excellent boilers could be and were produced to suit a wide variety of locomotives. Begun in 1902–3, they sufficed for the main GWR classes until the end of steam. It is remarkable that one of the secrets of the success of these boilers was an increase of just one inch on the minimum width of the firebox water legs, from the usual 2½in to 3½in. This made for better circulation of the water, quicker release of the steam bubbles, and less tendency for the firebox plates to burn. This apparently very small change was just as effective, indeed revolutionary in its effects, as the other very small increase in the lap of the valves. Seldom if ever can such tiny increases in dimensions, an inch or less on large locomotives, have made such a huge difference to efficiency.

7
Additions to the standard range

It is very noticeable that the proposed classes covered only the heavy main line work. No designs were included for shunting, branch line, or lighter work generally. There was a very good reason for this. The Great Western already had ample stocks of engines for such duties, many of them quite new, or still being built. There were 1,000 or more 0–6–0 saddle tanks, and the small Wolverhampton variety with 4ft 1in wheels continued to be built there until 1905. The last Dean Goods and the last batch of Metro 2–4–0 tank engines had been turned out as late as 1899. The thirty-one 2–4–2 tanks for suburban traffic were even then being constructed. For the lighter passenger work there were some 74 modern double-frame 4–4–0s with 6ft 8in wheels, about 120 'single drivers', some quite new, and many 2–4–0s of several varieties. The very useful Bulldog 4–4–0s with 5ft 8in wheels went on being built until 1906, and there were already about 40 Dukes. The Aberdare 2–6–0s continued to be built up to 1906, until the class totalled 80.

The truth is that had the rate of usage not been very light, the GWR would have already had more engines than it really needed. This no doubt is the reason for the surprising fact that the annual rate of new construction during Churchward's regime was considerably lower than it was under any of the other chiefs since Gooch. The average figures were 67 per annum for Armstrong and Hawksworth, 72 for Dean, 112 for Collett, but only 56 for Churchward.

We have just seen that Churchward's original scheme only provided for the larger main line engines, as there were plenty of smaller ones. However, he very soon made one exception, and in so doing produced one of his most unusual and enterprising conceptions. This was the small 2–6–2 tank, a thoroughly modern design for branch line work. It included almost all his standard features on a

Small 2–6–2 tank of the 4575 class, from the later Collett series with large tanks, built with superheater and top feed

reduced scale: the taper boiler with the carefully shaped firebox, the Standard No 5 boiler, the same basic design of cylinders, valves and motion, and the very sound and reliable axleboxes. There was one rather surprising exception. A notable and unusual feature of all his larger 2-cylinder engines was the 30in stroke, with an 18in bore to the cylinders, giving a high ratio of stroke to bore. This was important both for pulling power, more leverage at the crank, and for expansive working. In these small tank engines, with 17in x 24in cylinders, the stroke/bore ratio was rather poor. One would have expected on Churchward's principles something more like 16in x 26in or even 15in x 28in.

The reason for this departure from principle was probably as follows. The pioneer small 2–6–2, No 115, and the first production batch, Nos 4401–10, had very small driving wheels, only 4ft 1½in diameter. Why this was done it is difficult to say. It was probably a 'carry-over' from the Wolverhampton 0–6–0 tanks, which had this size. This first batch of engines also had smaller diameter cylinders, 16½in, which gave a slightly better ratio, and it was probably considered unwise to use cranks with more than 12in throw with such small wheels.

These first eleven engines, the 44xx class, did however prove very useful in a limited sphere, for until it was closed in March 1956 they almost monopolised the work on the Princetown branch, which climbed some 1,200 feet in about 12 miles. They were also used in later years on the Much Wenlock branch in Shropshire, another line which had to gain a lot of altitude in a very few miles.

Anyway, experience showed that for most duties somewhat larger wheels were desirable. The next batch, Nos 4500–19, had 4ft 7½in driving wheels, and to keep up the tractive effort, the cylinders were bored out to 17in, still with the 24in stroke; the boiler pressure was raised from 165lb/sq in 180lb/sq in. It was later increased to 200lb/sq in on the 45xx, 180lb/sq in on the 44xx. The 45xx class were a great success, and eventually numbered 175 engines. The last 100, the 4575 class, had tapered side tanks, with an increased water capacity.

It has been said that with their liveliness and good acceleration, they revolutionised the work of West Country branches, and were regarded by their crews with respect and affection, sometimes even with awe. It is probably fair to say that they were the best small branch line tank engines ever built in this country. They were speedy, running easily at 60mph, thanks no doubt to their modern cylinder design and valve events. They were also remarkably powerful for their size. Before the Kingswear line was upgraded to take Castles and Kings, these little engines used to replace the main line

Churchward mixed traffic 2–6–0, No 6312, as fitted with outside steam pipes in 1948. (*A. R. Brown*)

Churchward's last design, his large mixed traffic 2–8–0 with 5ft 8in wheels; illustrated is No 4707

engines at Paignton, and haul the Torbay expresses over the 1 in 60 grades to Kingswear.

In doing so they would take up to ten main line corridor coaches, 360 tons, without any trouble. I now own a replica 5in gauge 2–6–2 tank approximately one-twelfth full size, and it is just as good as the originals — free-running, sure-footed, a very good steamer. It surprises everyone by its power, working hard all through the summer pulling heavy loads of passengers on the railway of the Bournemouth & District Society of Model Engineers, of which I am a member.

The LMS tried to produce a similar engine a quarter of a century later around 1930, but the result was a miserable flop. E. S. Cox has told us that in the Derby Drawing Office at that time there was a 'Law of the Medes and Persians' which no one dared to alter. Presumably because S. W. Johnson's admirable little 0–6–0 tender engines had a wheelbase of 8ft 0in plus 8ft 6in, there was a hard-and-fast rule that any six-coupled engine, whatever its size or wheel arrangement, must have this coupled wheelbase. Whether this rule was enforced by the civil engineer or by the chief draughtsman is not clear, but enforced it was. As a result, when a class of light 2–6–2 tank engines came to be designed it had to have the sacred 16ft 6in wheelbase.

This made the engine far too long for its purpose, adding much useless weight, and taking up too much space in bay platforms and the like. It must have caused trouble on sharp curves and turn-outs. In contrast the coupled wheelbase of the GWR 45xx class was 11ft 6in.

Because of the unnecessary dead weight caused by the excessive length on the LMS engines (nominally of Fowler design), the boiler had to be kept very small to save weight. In his most interesting and delightful book, *Living with London Midland Locomotives*, John Powell describes how 'these wretched machines, whose boiler would not have supplied enough heat to mash tea in a good sized refreshment room, staggered about the branch lines of the system'. They had very old-fashioned cylinders and valve gear, so could not make good use of what little steam there was, and they weighed 72 tons, compared with 57 tons for the earlier GWR engines, and 61 tons for the later ones. Even when Stanier brought out further batches of 2–6–2 tanks for the LMS, with taper boiler and improved valve events, they were not much better; the proportions were all wrong from the beginning. The Great Western 'Small Prairies', as they have sometimes been called, were in a class by themselves, one of Churchward's very successful innovations.

We have seen that by 1904 Churchward had produced prototypes

2–8–0 tank No 4260, at Gloucester in 1935. This class was built in large numbers for South Wales coal traffic

for his standard range — a range which could be and was easily extended later to include the very successful 2–6–0 mixed-traffic engines, and the numerous 2–8–0 tanks for the South Wales coal traffic. Harold Holcroft has related how Churchward came up to his drawing board one day in 1910 and said, 'Very well then, get me out a 2–6–0 with 5ft 8in wheels, outside cylinders, the No 4 boiler, and bring in all the standard details you can'. This simple 'new mix' of the standard parts, the 43xx class, was the start of a revolution, for it inaugurated the vogue of the general utility engine.

Thus Churchward had laid the foundation for a range of standard designs — simple, reliable, efficient — which because of the standardisation of parts could be quickly and economically turned out and did not require a huge and varied stock of spares. The scheme was intended to suffice for 20 years or more. It did in fact last out steam, over a period of no less than 60 years.

It is rather surprising that he did not leave things there. With hindsight it might have been better if he had. The Americans later showed how two cylinders could suffice for the largest and fastest express engines. The Milwaukee Road 4–6–4s used on the 'Hiawatha' were known to average 98mph over 60 miles, and attain 120mph. The immense 4–8–4s of the Union Pacific attained over 100mph on the level with 900-ton trains. A 'Super Saint' with the King boiler, 250lb/sq in boiler pressure, and 21in x 30in cylinders, could have done all that the Kings could do. It would have been a good deal cheaper to build and maintain. But it was not to be — Churchward was diverted from his path of simplicity, seduced by the wiles of the 'Frenchmen'.

8

The 'Frenchmen' and what followed

Many people have wondered why the three de Glehn Compound Atlantics, Nos 102–4, were purchased. I believe that it was simply this. Churchward as a very sound and practical engineer wanted to have a 'control' for his experiments. Before building his revolutionary engines (as they then were) in quantity he wisely decided to make sure that he was on the right lines, and that his engines really would be the best possible at that time. The de Glehn du Bousquet 4–4–2s of the Nord Railway in France than had the reputation of being the finest express engines in the world. Their reputation for fast and economical running was such that they were widely copied elsewhere, and even the Pennsylvania Railroad in the United States bought one to try out.

Churchward persuaded the board of directors to buy No 102 *La France* in 1903. He was determined that competition between his engines and their foreign rival should be fair and equal. So No 171 *Albion*, (the significance of the name vis-á-vis *La France* is obvious) was built to the same design as No 98, but with a boiler pressure of 225lb/sq in, as near as may be to the 227lb/sq in of the French engine. Such people as Webb and T. W. Worsdell had set compound engines with 175lb/sq in pressure to compete against simple engines with only 150lb/sq in, because they wanted to 'prove' that compounds were better. Churchward even had *Albion* altered to a 4–4–2 after a short time to ensure that the comparison was as fair as possible.

In a series of trials *Albion* proved just as powerful and just as fast as *La France* and surprisingly slightly more economical in coal, just where a compound would be expected to excel. The 2-cylinder simple naturally used less oil, was much cheaper to build, and very much easier and cheaper to maintain. The French engine was a very complicated 'box of tricks', with four sets of valve gear, independently adjustable cut-offs for high pressure and low pressure, an elaborate system of changeover valves for 'simple' working, a complex variable blast-pipe, and so on. The British engine was therefore much more suitable for handling by ordinary British drivers, who were not highly trained engineers like their French counterparts. The economy of *Albion* is simply explained. The excellent valve gear made it possible to run at 22 to 25 percent cut-off, where the compound on similar work needed about 55 percent. The expansion ratio was about the same.

Altogether, the result was a triumph for Churchward, and proved that he could not do better than go ahead with his plan, and multiply his standard prototypes. However, individual engines do differ in performance. Some people, surprised at the outcome of the trials, seem to have suggested that *La France* was below par, not so good as most of its sisters on the Nord. (It is possible that the shorter chimney, to fit in with the British loading gauge, could have impaired the steaming slightly.) To make doubly sure, in 1905 Churchward obtained two more French Compounds, No 103, later named *President*, and No 104, which became *Alliance*, as the Entente Cordiale was much in the news at the time. These were slightly larger and more powerful than *La France*, being of the later Paris–Orleans design. However, any improvement in performance was insufficient to justify a change of course.

Professor W. A. Tuplin once suggested in an article that the French Compounds were failures. This is far from the truth. All remained in service for over 20 years, so they must have been worth keeping. Churchward spoke highly of *La France*. In 1904, during the discussion after Monsieur Sauvage had read a paper on compound locomotives to the institution of Mechnaical Engineers, Churchward said that on the Great Western they had two or three engines which could sustain a drawbar pull of over two tons at 70mph, and 'one of them was *La France*'. The other two would doubtless have been Nos 98 and 171 *Albion*. The fact that *Alliance* was fitted with a standard Swindon No 1 boiler after only two years' service did not mean as some have thought that its own boiler was no good. Churchward had introduced the excellent system of having a float of spare boilers for his standard classes. He was I believe the first engineer to do this, though it later became general practice. Without this provision, engines wasted much time out of traffic, cluttering up the shops, while the frames stood idle waiting for the boiler to come back from overhaul. By fitting a new or repaired boiler from the pool the engine could be back in traffic in half the time or less. The only way to provide spare boilers for the French engines was to adapt them to carry Swindon boilers. Two years later No 104 got its own boiler back, then had the boiler from No 103. No 103 had a Swindon boiler after five years, then the one from No 104, and so on. *La France* kept its own boiler until 1916, but then also had a Swindon No 1. The company would not have gone to this trouble and expense if the three compounds had not been useful and efficient engines. In fact Holcroft once stated that in looking over the dynamometer car rolls at Swindon (probably about 1910) the highest drawbar horsepower he found was achieved by No 103 on a Birmingham express. This was at around 45mph. There is little doubt that at 60–70mph a Star or Saint would do better. Even so, the French engines were not failures at all, they were very good.

As a result of experience with the 'Frenchmen' Churchward found there was no advantage to be gained from compounding. From them however he derived two excellent features. One was the de Glehn bogie, with the weight applied by brackets under or outside the frames, with hemispherical bearings in cups known as 'spittoons', which in turn could slide on a flat surface on the bogie frame. This provided a wide base, making for a steadier engine and lessening the tendency to roll. The bogies for the standard engines were of a pure American type, with bar frames and swing-link side control.

These were redesigned from 1908 onwards to have the de Glehn side-bearers and spring lateral control, and the earlier bogies were converted. If only the bar frames which gave much trouble had been replaced by plate frames this bogie might have been the best ever. It had the excellent Adams system of springing, with one inverted plate spring each side, with a cradle bearing on the two axleboxes, and an adequate wheelbase of 7ft. The de Glehn side-bearers and spring side control were later used on the Southern Railway. Stanier took them to the LMS, whence they were inherited by British Rail. It has been widely believed that it was only this admirable bogie which averted an appalling accident in Crewe Station, when *Coronation* had a go at the speed record, and not having Great Western brakes,

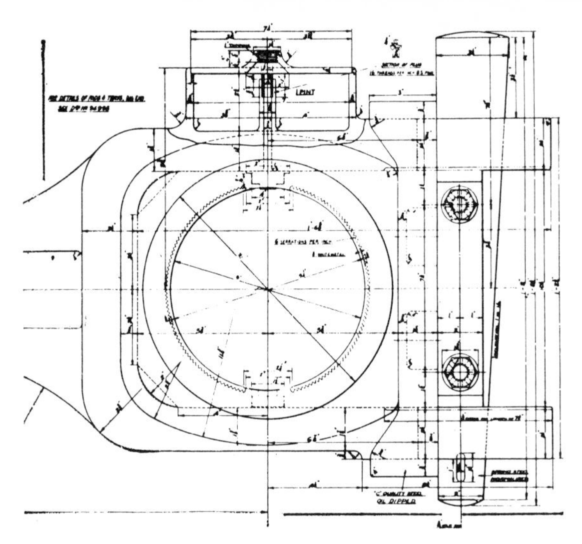

Drawing of de Glehn pattern inside connecting rod big-end, as used on all GWR four-cylinder locomotives

was unable to stop in time.

The other detail which Churchward adopted for his 4-cylinder engines, was the excellent French pattern big-end for the inside connecting rods, which proved remarkably trouble-free. The end of the rod was forked to contain the bearing brasses; the ends of the fork were gripped by a very strong and substantial clip. This was held in place against the brasses by a tapered cotter, this last passing through slots in the prongs of the fork. The cotter itself was driven home, and secured by set-bolts with locking plates, and a small cotter which passed through a slot in the large one below the clip. This big-end was used by Stanier on his LMS Pacifics, also on the final British express design, No 71000 *Duke of Gloucester*. When K. J. Cook was moved by the British Rail authorities from Swindon to Doncaster, he started fitting these big-ends to the inside connecting rods of Gresley Pacifics, with excellent results in reducing their deplorable tendency to run hot. They had previously had a particularly pernicious variant of the already suspect marine big-end, which was just not rigid enough for the job.

The other feature of the French engines which attracted Churchward was the good balance and smooth running which resulted from having on each side of the engine cranks at 180 degrees and two

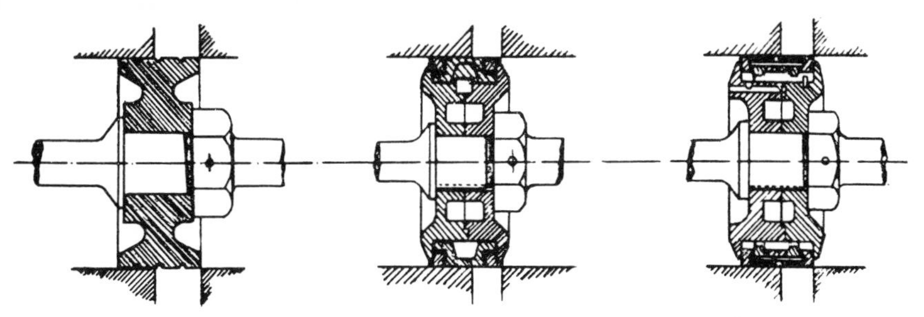

Piston valves: plug, L-ring, and semi-plug. (*Courtesy Allen & Unwin*)

pistons moving in opposite directions. It was undoubtedly this which induced him to depart from his ideals of standardisation and simplicity, and launch out on 4-cylinder engines.

Before we start considering the 4-cylinder engines it is necessary to say something about piston valves and superheaters. First, piston valves. Churchward soon realised that to get the large port openings he saw to be essential for power at speed, slide valves would have to be impossibly big. They would take up too much room and create immense friction. So piston valves were a 'must'. Unfortunately they present a number of problems, especially steam leakage to exhaust, and the trapping of water in the cylinders. Slide valves, if they and the port face are properly made and finished, are inherently self-sealing, due to the steam pressure on the back of the valve. If water is trapped in the cylinder, or excessive compression occurs for any reason, the valve can lift and relieve the pressure. As a slide valve wears, provided there is no serious scoring, the seal tends if anything to improve. There is a traditional saying that 'piston valves wear out but slide valves wear in'.

Piston valves have none of these advantages. The earliest examples, tried in the middle of the nineteenth century, proved disastrous. There was no provision for the release of trapped water, so cylinders were smashed. In the early 1890s, W. M. Smith, chief draughtsman on the North Eastern Railway, designed and patented a piston valve. This had an ingenious but complicated arrangement of collapsible piston rings, to seal against leakage, but to release water when necessary. These do not seem to have been entirely successful. They were used both on the North Eastern and the Midland, but in several cases there was a reversion to slide valves, though the use of

French Compound 4–4–2 No 102 *La France* when new, in lined black, at Bath

piston valves was resumed later, presumably after improvements had been made.

The first piston valves tried on the GWR were on the last few of the 2721 class of saddle tanks, built in 1900. This was a peculiar arrangement in which piston valves of a 'plug' type, ie, with oil grooves but no rings, were situated between the cylinders. Both valves were on the centre-line, the upper one serving the right-hand cylinder and the lower one the left-hand. The valves were driven directly by offset arms from the normal Stephenson gear, a far from ideal arrangement which must have caused bending stresses and friction. In this position the valves had to be of small diameter from lack of space. A similar arrangement was incorporated in the first batches of the 2–4–2 tank engines, the 3600 class. The design was not a success. A reversion to the ordinary back-to-back slide valves was made in the last batch of the 2–4–2s and the earlier ones altered to correspond. The same alteration was carried out rather more slowly with the saddle tanks.

There was much steam leakage with the plain 'plug' valves, as might be expected, although trapped water was dealt with by large relief valves on the cylinder covers. These last proved effective and were used on all subsequent piston valve cylinders.

For the standard outside-cylinder engines something better than the leaky 'plug' valves was clearly required. At first Churchward used an American design of valve known as the 'L ring'. These as the name implies had outer spring rings of an L shape, with a bull ring between them. These valves had the advantage of providing a sharp opening to steam, and an equally quick and definite cut-off. They were however stiff and rigid, not adapting easily to any wear, and they caused rather a lot of friction.

After a few years the semi-plug valve was introduced in the USA. Churchward at once saw its advantages, and obtained the manufacturing rights for Great Britain. In these valves the rings were pressed outwards to the liners by steam pressure, and locked in position by wedge rings, so that they automatically adjusted themselves to the bore. When the steam was shut-off, the rings could contract clear of the liners, so that there was then hardly any friction and coasting was very free. In fact they combined some of the advantages of both slide and piston valves. They required great precision and accuracy in manufacture, but the machine shop at Swindon soon mastered the art. All valves were sent out complete and ready for insertion, and no attempt was allowed to make or assemble them at the lesser works or running sheds. Thus made to the highest standards they provided the answer to the problems, and from that time the Great Western used no other.

A great injustice is often done to Churchward over superheating. He was the true pioneer of this immense improvement in Britain,

French Compound 4–4–2 No 103 *President*, in original state, at Bath

French Compound 4–4–2 No 104 *Alliance*, with Swindon No 1 boiler, superheater, and top feed

though few writers have recognised the fact. I have read that the first application of a superheater to a British locomotive was by Hughes on the Lancashire & Yorkshire Railway in 1908. In another book I have seen it stated that Earle Marsh on the London, Brighton & South Coast was the first in 1909.

We can ignore Aspinall's experiments on the Lancashire & Yorkshire Railway, about 1900, when he fitted his own design of smokebox superheater to some of his Atlantics, and the experimental fitting of the Phoenix smokebox superheater to one or two engines on the Highland, the North British and the Great Northern of Ireland. It has been said of smokebox superheaters that they 'combine minimal superheat with maximum nuisance value'.

Churchward was quite definitely the first to fit a proper fire-tube superheater, when No 2901 *Lady Superior* was built new with a Schmidt design in May 1906. Hughes followed, in November 1906, when he rebuilt two 0–6–0 goods engines. Churchward seems to have found two disadvantages to the Schmidt pattern, for he never used it again. One was inaccessibility of the elements. In the conventional type of superheater, Schmidt or Schmidt-based, it is only possible to remove a faulty element in the top row by removing two other elements first. Also, the superheat temperature was probably too high for the oils and lubricators of the period, causing a serious build-up of hard carbon in steamchests and blastpipe.

Churchward next tried the American Cole superheater, which was of the field tube type, in which the outward flow tube in each element fitted inside the return flow tube, being open-ended and of smaller diameter. This was fitted to No 4010 *Western Star* in 1907. In this inaccessibility of the elements was even worse, so the Swindon No 1 superheater was designed, and fitted to No 4011 *Knight of the Garter* in 1908. It was also tried on No 111 in *The Great Bear*, built in the same year. This was of the field tube pattern like the Cole, but re-designed to make each element easily removable. The Swindon No 2 was similar, but with normal return tube elements, with hairpin bends at the firebox end, in place of the field tubes. This was tried on No 2922 *Saint Gabriel* later in 1908. Then followed the Swindon No 3, which was fitted to No 4021 *King Edward*. This became the standard type, and was rapidly fitted to many classes, not only the larger engines, but also to such as the Dean Goods. It was cheap and simple, and it had the great advantage that any one element could be removed and replaced without disturbing any other. Its main dis-advantage was that the layout only permitted the fitting of two rows of elements, 12 in the No 2 boiler, 14 in the standard Class 1, 4, and 8 boilers, the latter fitted to Collett's Castles. Only in the largest boilers, Nos 7 and 12, fitted to class 47xx locomotives and Kings respectively, was it possible to have 16 elements. In fact in the later Class 2 boilers, used mainly on Bulldogs and 2–6–2 tanks, there was only one row of flues with six elements, and this was standard from the beginning in the smaller engines, including the 45xx.

Later on, when deteriorating quality of coal and maintenance made higher superheat necessary, Hawksworth had to revert to the Schmidt pattern to get in three rows, and then four. The vast majority of the engines retained the Swindon pattern to the end of steam. Its cheapness and simplicity made it easy to fit to large numbers of both new and existing engines in a short time, and by 1914 when the war slowed the work down, the Great Western had over 800 superheated engines in service, a far larger number than any other line.

It is true that the Swindon superheater provided less heating surface and increase in temperature than the Schmidt-based designs. Churchward has often been criticised for this, unfairly in my opinion. Some writers have tried to maintain that the Swindon superheater was only a 'steam drier'. This was nonsense. Steam temperature rises with pressure, and at that time the Great Western was using 225lb/sq in when other lines very rarely went above 180lb/sq in and often *reduced* the pressure to 160lb/sq in or even 150lb/sq in when changing to superheat. Swindon boilers were starting at a higher temperature, and a very high increment would have made the final temperature too high for the oils then available. As it was, some other railways experienced serious lubrication difficulties, overheating of pistons and valves, and valve ports and blastpipes getting choked with carbon deposits. We must remember that Churchward was first in the field, both in fitting the first superheater, and also in applying superheating on a large scale. For the circumstances and oils of the period, he was absolutely right. It was Collett who was at fault in not making the change to larger superheaters when times had changed, oils improved and coal deteriorated.

9

The great enigma: The 4-cylinder engines.

We now come to the great enigma, the 4-cylinder engines. There is little doubt that they were the most succesful family of express engines ever built, certainly in Great Britain, possibly in the world. Look at their achievements. For nearly 60 years, with some modifications and enlargements, this basic design provided the principal express engines of a very large and great railway. Nothing better was ever required while steam remained. At the end of their careers, when over 30 years old, the double-chimney high superheat Kings were as capable as any other engines in the country, at least for runs up to 200 miles and with tolerable coal. Yet they were just enlarged, superheated versions of Churchward's Stars of 1907.

In their day, the Stars, Castles and Kings ran what was almost certainly the best express train service in the world, taking into account variety of route and frequency, as well as average speed. Other railway companies here and abroad ran a few crack expresses on a limited set of routes. Not so the Great Western. The expresses to Devon and Cornwall had the galloping ground through Slough and Maidenhead, the mountainous grades of the West Country, and all the varied and rather curvaceous miles in between, to be tackled by the same engine in one trip. There were the high-speed trains between London and Bristol, the very heavy South Wales trains via the Severn Tunnel, and the Oxford, Worcester and Hereford services, on which the first well authenticated 100mph was reached. There were two separate North-to-West routes, one via Hereford and Shrewsbury, the other through Cheltenham and Stratford-on-Avon. The hardest work of all was done on the highly competitive, hilly, slack-infested Birmingham route. Good work was also done on the extension of that route to Shrewsbury and Chester. The engines did all this with notable economy and reliability. They were famous both for smoth riding and sure-footedness: they were far better at starting than the various Pacifics, or their main 4–6–0 rivals, the LMS Royal Scots.

I was very amused a few years ago, when a gentleman who had a very distinguished career in the Derby drawing office wrote to the *Model Engineer* averring that the Castles would never have stood up to the hard work done by the Royal Scots. I wrote back, pointing out that some of the earlier Castles lasted nearly 40 years in heavy express service, whereas all the Royal Scots, after from 16 to 20 years' service, had to 'have their cabs jacked up, and new engines put underneath'. The so-called 'rebuilds' cannot have incorporated very much else; the 'rebuilt' Scots were a fresh design. Even the wheels were different, I believe, of Stanier pattern with triangular rims and bolted-on balance weights. I am afraid that the Derby man was very angry at what I wrote, and described me as a blind Swindon fanatic. A 'blind Swindon fanatic' would hardly have written so critical a book as this!

The record of service of the Great Western 4-cylinder 4–6–0s was a wonderful one, possibly unequalled in any country in the world through the whole period of steam traction. Yet here is the enigma. In some respects they were a bad design. They threw a spanner right into the works of Churchward's logical and tidy scheme for a range of simple, robust, standard locomotives, having many components interchangeable between the different classes. They were expensive to build, inaccessible and complicated to maintain. They seemed quite out of keeping with Churchward's usual outlook and way of doing things. However did they come to be built? When the Stars were designed, the 2-cylinder Saints were doing the work admirably, and were quite adequate for years to come. Later, when some enlargement was needed, it was desired to use the excellent Standard No 7 boiler as fitted to the 47xx class 2–8–0s, but a 4-cylinder engine thus equipped would have proved too heavy for the civil engineer's approval. Because of this, the Castles had to be a compromise with a smaller boiler than the Standard No 7, and had therefore little reserve to cope with bad coal or other difficult circumstances. The Saints were officially stated to be three tons lighter than the Stars, though having the same boiler and overall dimensions. It would seem probable therefore, that had Collett enlarged the Saint instead of the

Star, he would have been able to use the larger and better proportioned Class 7 boiler, without exceeding the weight limit.

We have already seen how an even larger Saint could have been built to do the work of the Kings. Experience with the French compounds had convinced Churchward that compounding was an unnecessary complication, but he does seem to have fallen for the better balance and smoother running made possible by the use of four cylinders, with cranks at 180 degrees on each side of the engine. There was also in theory at any rate the possibility of a considerable reduction in the 'hammer-blow' and its bad effect on the track, with a 4-cylinder engine. 'Hammer blow' is caused by the proportion of the balance weights used to offset the reciprocating motion of pistons, crossheads and other parts, as distinct from the proportion used to counter revolving weights. But in the Great Western engines full advantage does not seem to have been taken of this possibility. They were provided with quite a high degree of reciprocating balance, even though it should not have really been necessary. Complaints of rough riding with 2-cylinder engines seem to have been much exaggerated, provided that the engines were well designed and properly maintained. I have ridden on British Railways Britannia class 4–6–2s on the Liverpool Street to Norwich line at speeds up to 90mph. I did not find it at all uncomfortable, nor was I very tired after travelling from London to Norwich and back in five hours. (The turnround time was much curtailed on one trip owing to many delays on the outward journey.) On only one engine out of the three on which I rode did I suffer any discomfort, and that engine was in a very run-down state, nearly due for general overhaul. On the other hand, a Sandringham 3-cylinder 4–6–0, recently overhauled, on which I rode on another occasion was so rough and uncomfortable that I was very glad to get off it, even though we did not run very fast.

O. S. Nock in his book *The Great Western Railway in the 20th Century*, describing a footplate trip on No 2934 *Butleigh Court* praises the smooth action and riding of the engine: 'She was almost as sweet running as a Castle' even though the engine was being driven at 20 percent cut-off'. The Saints were great favourites with the enginemen. They would not have been had they been seriously rough and uncomfortable to ride on.

On the Great Western Stars, Churchward was at pains to keep all

Star class four-cylinder 4–6–0 No 4047 *Princess Louise*. This was one of a late series built with superheater, top feed etc

four connecting rods the same length, again in the interests of good balance. This meant fixing the outside cylinders to the frames just where the latter were weakest, because they had to be cut away to allow for the side movement of the trailing wheels of the bogie. To withstand the racking strains caused by the pull and push of the outside cylinders, a massive horizontal cast-steel cross-member had to be provided, to brace the frames at this point. This 'buried' the inside valve gear, already difficult to get at for oiling, examination and maintenance, and made the inaccessibility much worse. On at least one occasion a Star was unable to take its train because the driver had got stuck trying to get at the valve gear, and could not be extricated in time. It is probable that this sort of thing happened on other occasions as well. This position for the cylinders, as against the usual place between the bogie wheels, had other disadvantages. The cutaway in the frames made it more difficult to fix the cylinders securely. The LMS Princess Royal 4–6–2s, based directly on Swindon practice and with the same layout, certainly suffered a good deal from cylinders working loose. It seems likely that this also happened on the Great Western, but if so, it was hushed up with customary Swindon cunning. Again, Harold Holcroft has told us of his attempts to work bigger cylinders into the design of *The Great Bear*, of a size to match the huge boiler. Because of the extra side movement of the bogie necessitated by the length of the 4–6–2 this proved to be impossible, and Churchward had to agree to the cylinder diameter remaining at 15in, the same as the Stars when superheated.

Now we come to the most extraordinary feature of the design, the inside Walschaert valve gear. This had another serious disadvantage, as well as being so hard to get at. There was the friction of two large eccentrics under heavy load, doing double duty driving two valves each, whereas the ballbearing return cranks commonly used with outside Walschaert gear are virtually frictionless. Tests in BR days showed that the Kings had unnusually high internal resistance at speed, showing itself in a very big drop from indicated horse power developed in the cylinders to power available at the drawbar. This seemed to puzzle commentators, but I believe it was mainly due to the friction of those large eccentrics with their high rubbing speed. Excellent as these 4-cylinder engines were in performance, they could and should have been better.

Why then were all the Stars, Castles and Kings fitted with Walschaert valve gear inside, when the main reason for this motion becoming almost universal the world over was its accessibility in the usual outside position? I believe it came about unintentionally and really by accident. It has been reported that Churchward considered

Four cylinder 4–6–0 No 4092, *Dunraven Castle*, the last engine of the second batch, which the author saw built in 1925

there was not room within the loading gauge for outside gear strong enough to work two valves. This is surely nonsense. Thanks to Brunel and the broad gauge, the GWR loading-gauge was appreciably wider than that on the LMS, one reason why Kings and Halls were not allowed on the London Midland Region in the 1948 Exchange Trials. Yet the LMS Duchesses worked two valves very successfully with outside gear. We must look for another reason.

Churchward had devised an extremely good arrangement of Stephenson valve gear for his standard engines, and there is little doubt that he would have liked to have used it for his 4-cylinder ones. To get room for four eccentrics and straps of sufficient width, it would have been necessary to place the cylinders and cranks further apart, and that would seriously reduce the length of the axlebox bearings, or the width of the crank webs, or both.

As it was, it became impossible to use the excellent arrangement of a sliding tray with a lubricating pad under the journal, so far as the crank axle was concerned, because of the close proximity of the crank web. This was one of the snags of the 4-cylinder arrangement, if a fairly minor one.

W. H. Pearce, the draughtsman who had worked out the Stephenson gear in detail, came up with a suggestion for a crossover gear, and made a wooden model to demonstrate it to Churchward. In this gear the right-hand expansion link was driven from the left-hand crosshead, and vice versa. This was of course in addition to the usual link driving the combination lever from its own crosshead. In this way, eccentrics were eliminated altogether, but the gear really had to be inside, so that the arangement of outside valves driven by rocker arms from the inside gear was entirely logical. It is true that an American named Young had designed an outside valve gear on the same principle, which went by his name. Young gear was however excessively complicated, and I am not sure if it was ever used. Imagine the difficulty of arranging a gear to drive an outside expansion link from the crosshead on the opposite side of the engine. In *The Steam Locomotive in America*, by A. W. Bruce, there is a diagram of the Young gear, but it is very difficult to puzzle out how it is supposed to work.

The crossover idea itself was far from new. A similar arrangement had been designed in the 1870s by a Belgian named Stévart, and used

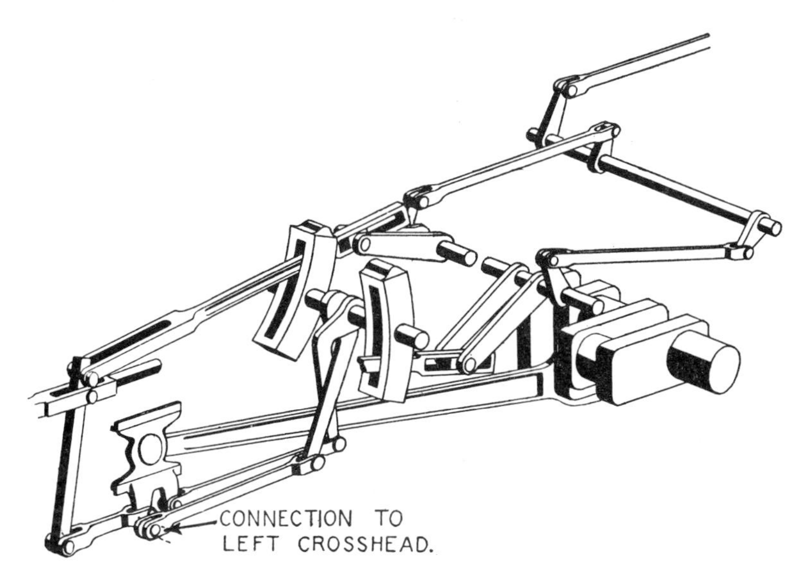

Scissors valve gear

on a few locomotives. Soon afterwards David Joy applied the same principle to marine engines. It is said that Pearce did not know that his idea had been forestalled, but it would seem that Churchward must have known, or made it his business to find out, otherwise a patent would surely have been applied for. Anyway, the valve gear designed by Pearce which became known colloquially as the 'scissors' gear, was fitted to the pioneer engine No 40 *North Star*.

It was never used again on the GWR, although *North Star* performed so well that it was followed by no fewer than 268 engines with the same cylinder arrangement. No 40 was originally built as a 4–4–2, doubtless for direct comparison with the two larger French compounds, but was rebuilt as a 4–6–0 after 3½ years. All subsequent 4-cylinder engines were built as 4–6–0s, as greater adhesion weight was found to be essential over heavy grades in all weathers. All had inside Walschaert valve gear of a rather unusual form, driving the outside valves by rocker arms, a strange and seemingly illogical arrangement. The sensible thing would have been to put the valve gear outside to work the outside valves, and use rocker arms to drive the inside ones, as on Claughtons and LSWR 'Paddleboats', as well as the LMS Duchesses.

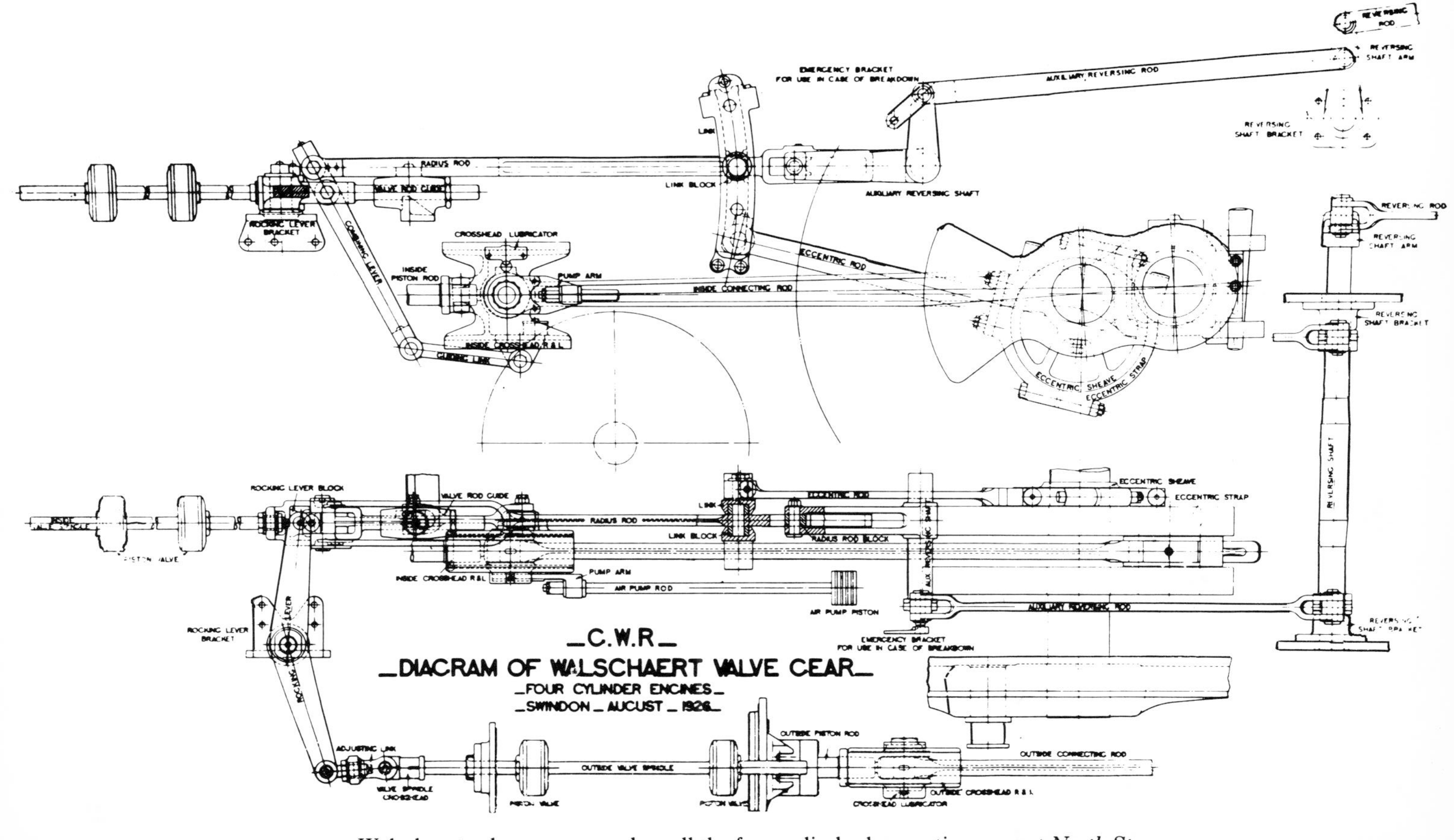

Walschaert valve gear as used on all the four-cylinder locomotives except *North Star*

Various reasons have been given and several theories advanced as to why the scissors gear was dropped like a hot potato and the Walschaert gear mounted inside where it was so inaccessible. By a strange coincidence, Robert Deeley, chief mechanical engineer of the Midland Railway, took out a patent for a cross-connected gear in 1906, a few months after *North Star* was built. As we have seen the principle was not new, having been tried many years before, so a patent could only apply to some novelty in lay-out or detail. Churchward was the first anyway in applying such a gear. Deeley's 4–4–0 No 990, the first engine to embody his design, was not built until 1907. Nevertheless Deeley, a notoriously hot-tempered man, is said to have written a very angry letter to Churchward, accusing him of infringing his patent, and threatening various penalties. The same reports say that Churchward replied telling Deeley to 'go to Hell'. This would be just what Churchward might be expected to do in the circumstances. His application of the gear was different from Deeley's. The latter had one expansion link about 18in in front of the other, so that the eccentric rods and radius rods had to be of widely differing lengths, which would not help in securing accurate valve events. This was done so that the cross-connections would clear one another in all positions. The Churchward-Pearce solution was quite different. The links were placed side-by-side, and driven by cross-over arms with a very peculiar and pronounced curvature to provide the necessary clearance. It was these arms that gave an impression of a pair of scissors, hence the name 'scissors gear' which did not apply to Deeley's arrangement at all.

The official reason for not continuing to use the scissors gear was that in the event of a breakdown the engine could not be worked home 'on one side'. But how often was that done, especially on the main lines of the GWR where in those days there were always standing pilots, spare engines kept ready in steam at all the principal stations? I should say hardly ever. In any case, if that had been the real reason, it could surely have been foreseen before No 40 was built, and would hardly have been serious enough to compel a sudden, almost panic change in design.

I believe this 'official reason' was a piece of window-dressing, to save face. The true reason was rather embarrassing, as no-one in the drawing office had foreseen it. To help in the deception, all the

4-cylinder engines, other than *North Star*, were provided with a small link attached to the auxillary reversing shaft arm, by which one half of the valve gear could easily be immobilised. Such a provision for a very unlikely need was unique in the locomotive world, and singularly unconvincing except as part of a cover-up.

Now for the real reason for the sudden change in design. The writer seems to have been almost the only person still living who knew, until in the *Echo* of the Great Western Society I told the story a few years ago, which was afterwards reproduced by the Railway Correspondence & Travel Society, in the final volume of its series on the *Locomotives of the Great Western Railway*. While serving as an apprentice in the 'A' erecting shop at Swindon, I asked Mr Jew, the assistant foreman, if I could work for a spell on the valve setting gang, to learn how it was done. He readily agreed, and I worked with the gang for a few weeks. On some railways it seems that almost any fitter was allowed to set valves, often with 'off-beat' effects which were all too obvious to the ear. This was not the position at Swindon. There, one small gang of experts under a chargeman did all the valve-setting in the 'A' shop. That meant all the engines built new and all the larger engines overhauled at Swindon. I worked closely during this period with the chargeman. He was a very interesting character as well as supremely expert at his job. He told me, and he of all men would have known, that the real trouble with the scissors gear was that it took ten days or a fortnight to set the valves, whereas I remember that we set the valves of one of the other Stars in little over a day.

I have already explained that the scissors gear had to have levers with a complicated curvature in two different planes to operate the links. Each lever was firmly welded to one of the trunnions of the link. If the valves were 'out', and with this tricky curvature of the arms they were almost sure to be at first, the whole assembly of link and arm had to be disconnected and taken down. The unwieldy and awkward object had to be manoeuvred out of a very cramped and inaccessible place under the boiler and between the wheels, and manhandled out of the pit and to the smithy. When the blacksmiths had altered it, there was an equally awkward job getting it back into position, and connecting it. Then the valve-setting process, which in those days involved six labourers moving the engine backwards and forwards with pinch bars, had to be gone through again. This whole costly, time-wasting business might have to be carried out two, three or even four times before the setting was absolutely right, as at Swindon it had to be.

The self-styled 'Premier Line', the London & North Western Railway, might be and often was content with two strong beats, a weak one, and the fourth almost non-existent. Other lines, too, might have put up with that sort of thing, but not (to its credit) the Great Western.

To return to No 40 *North Star* and the scissors gear, the time-consuming process could just be tolerated with one engine when it would be needed about once in two years. It was out of the question with a large class. *North Star* did in fact retain the scissors gear for 23 years until rebuilt as a Castle with the normal Walschaert gear in 1929. For the whole batch of 4-cylinder 4–6–0s already planned, it was essential to do something different, and a hurried decision must have been taken. It was too late to re-design the engines to have outside valve gear. Churchward's position was not too easy at that time. After four years in office, he had not yet gained the confidence of all the board. My father knew Charles Mortimer, who was one of the directors, and who had a Badminton 4–4–0 named after him. When my father was rather enthusiastic about Churchward's fine new engines, Mortimer would have none of it: 'Unnecessarily big and heavy, causing us to spend too much money on track and bridges', he said, 'and too expensive to build'.

It would never do for Churchward at that critical time to let it be known that he had blundered. The remedy for the difficulty with *North Star* had to be found quickly. It was desirable that it should be unobtrusive, so that the change would scarcely be noticeable to non-professionals.

The first batch of 4-cylinder 4–6–0s, Nos 4001–10, the Stars proper, began to appear in traffic barely ten months after *North Star*. To achieve this required a quick and simple change in design. All that was done in fact was to leave the valve gear exactly as it was, except that the scissors arms and the rods connecting them to the opposite crossheads were deleted, and in their place a pair of eccentrics, straps and rods fitted to drive expansion links of the same type and in the same position. It was in fact a very simple change, involving just the six new parts per engine. So the fitting of

Walschaert gear *inside* was really a kind of accident, a hasty improvisation to remedy and cover up an unforeseen snag to the crossover gear.

All this is very understandable. What is hard to understand and condone is the continuation of this rather makeshift and very inaccessible arrangement on 268 engines, Stars, Castles and Kings, built over a period of 43 years. One would have thought something better could and should have been devised. Collett however had not been trained on a railway at all, but with a general engineering firm of very high reputation, Maudslay, Son & Field. He was a very competent workshop and production engineer, but no locomotive designer. As we shall see in a later chapter, his one and only attempt at novelty in design ran into grave difficulty, and he never tried to do anything original after that. It is also fair to say that both Castles and Kings were designed and produced with very great haste for reasons of prestige. Sir Felix Pole, the very strong and dynamic general manager in the 1920s, would not tolerate the Great Western coming second to any other railway in the 'tractive effort stakes'. The Castle design was rushed out in haste to compete with the first Gresley Pacifics, and the Kings produced just as hurriedly to put the Southern Lord Nelsons in their place.

What is really extraordinary was the proposal to use the same valve gear arrangement in the 'Super Pacific' design which was roughed-out under Hawksworth during the second world war, to be the prestige express engine after the war, had the GWR continued in existence. Although Churchward himself had been such a great pioneer and innovater, both his successors remained firmly 'tied to his apron strings' all their days, except that Hawksworth did go in for increased superheat, which Collett refused to do, even after Stanier had told him of its success on the LMS.

Nevertheless, as we have seen, the 4-cylinder engines achieved remarkable success. The Stars in particular were a beautifully proportioned design. As first built, with 14¼in diameter cylinders, 26in stroke and 8in piston valves, excellent ratios were achieved. They were still very good when the cylinder bore was increased to 15in after superheating. Although the Castles gained most of the limelight and were built in much larger numbers than the Stars or Kings, they were not, size for size, such good engines as the Stars, and the reasons are not far to seek. Some of the class put up very fine performances, but they were not very consistent. O. S. Nock, after timing innumerable runs both from the train and from the footplate, has said that he never knew a large class where the standard of performance differed so much from one engine to another. It is very noticeable that many of the best recorded performances were with the same few engines. For example, take the first ten of the class. Whenever a really good performance was sought, it seemed as if the engine chosen was always either No 4074 *Caldicot Castle*, or No 4079 *Pendennis Castle*. Soon after the first batch appeared, it was quite naturally desired to have dynamometer car trials to see what they could do in developing sustained power and speed with economy of coal. It would have been expected that the pioneer which had had the most publicity, including a very popular book named after it, No 4073 *Caerphilly Castle*, would be used. But no, *Caldicot Castle* was chosen. There seems to be no record ever published of *Caerphilly Castle* itself doing anything special. In 1925 came the famous Exchange Trials with the LNER, which not only gained much glory for the GWR but also persuaded Gresley to modify the valve gear on his Pacifics on Great Western principles, and so ensured their success. Once again it was *Caldicot Castle* and *Pendennis Castle* which were picked for the contest. *Pendennis Castle* was turned out for the Cornish Riviera Express when Cecil J. Allen was to ride the footplate, and publish details of the performance in *The Railway Magazine*. A little later No 5000 *Launceston Castle* became the star performer, used on the extra fast publicity-seeking runs of the Cheltenham Flyer, and sent to the LMS to show how to build an efficient engine.

Mr Nock noted a higher drawbar horsepower with Star No 4042 *Prince Albert*, than he ever experienced with a Castle. I was working on the Great Western when the second batch of Castles Nos 4083–92 was turned out in 1925, and a number of the senior drivers who had experience with the first ten said that 'they ought to build more Stars'. They preferred them.

As we have seen, the Castles were a compromise design, especially where the size of the boiler was concerned. The enlargement of the Star was uneven. For example, the already moderate size superheater on the Star was reproduced exactly in the larger boiler of the Castle, to supply considerably larger cylinders, while the increase in grate area and heating surface was not quite in proportion. It was the almost unanimous opinion among the running inspectors that the No 1 boiler, used on Stars, Saints and 28xx 2–8–0s was for its size the best-proportioned and most satisfactory of all the standard boilers. During and after the second world war when quality of coal and quite often the standard of firing deteriorated sharply, it was the Castles which seemed the worst affected.

When we look at the cylinders, the departure from Churchward's ideal proportions was even more marked. Eight-inch piston valves, generous for 14¼ cylinders and very adequate for 15in, were not ideal for the 16in, which might be enlarged to 17in by successive reboring. Again, the stroke/bore ratio grew less good with each increase in bore. In the design of the Kings, using 9in valves and increasing the stroke to 28in went a long way toward bringing proportions back to the Star ideal. Several writers with much experience on the footplate have testified that so long as the fireman could cope with the very long grate, Kings were more reliable steamers than the Castles, and much quicker to recover boiler pressure if it was dropped. Kenneth Leech has maintained that the Kings were definitely more free-running than the Castles. This would doubtless be due to their bigger valves.

I have mentioned in Chapter 11 how rushed the drawing office was in the first few years after the grouping. The working drawings issued to the shops for the first batches of Castles were just Star drawings, modified in red ink! This was only feasible because the designs were very nearly identical. On the next row of pits to where I was working in 1925 I saw and passed every day the second Star being converted to a Castle, No 4016 *Knight of the Golden Fleece*. (The first had been No 4009 *Shooting Star*, six months earlier.) The job was really very simple. Nearly all the parts, already stamped with the engine number, were used again. Extensions were added by electric arc-welding to the back end of the frames, and the only new parts were boiler, cylinders and cab. The increases in size were, 12in on frames and outer firebox length, 1in on cylinder diameter, and 3in on boiler diameter.

The Kings were much nearer to being a logical and well-proportioned enlargement of the Stars, and the increase in power was considerable. Their power and weight however did lead to a good deal of trouble with broken engine and bogie frames, and some modification was needed to springing before they became safe and smooth-riding. The very short, stiff bogie springs could remove all weight from their wheels, if there was a low place in the track. After No 6003 *King George IV* derailed its bogie near Midgham while running the down Cornish Riviera; coil springs had to be added to supplement the front bogie springs. Later on, a strong tendency to rolling and yawing at speed had to be dealt with, by doing away with the side play originally provided to the trailing coupled wheels, and providing them with much more flexible springs, having more but thinner plates. Only then did the Kings become very good riders. There is little doubt that the Kings were signficantly overweight. Officially, the weight of the engine alone was always quoted at 89 tons in working order, with 22 tons 10 cwt on each coupled axle. These figures are suspiciously exact, especially as they were still quoted after a number of additions had been made, such as four-row superheaters, strengthening pieces welded to the bogie frames, and patches on the main frames. The weight as first built is believed to have been around 93 tons, which could have grown to 94 or 95 tons in their old age.

Swindon seems to have been adept at 'cooking' the weights for the benefit of the civil engineer and the board. We have already judged that the Gooch 8ft singles must have been heavier than they were made out to be. The trick seems to have been to weigh the engines with the water level very low, the sandboxes empty, and an absolute minimum of coal on the grate. Many of the Welsh engines taken-over at the Grouping were quoted as being from three to five tons lighter, even after being fitted with new boilers carrying a higher pressure, enlarged bunkers and other features which could be expected to increase the weight. All rather suspicious.

Deception of this kind was doubtless made easier by the very strong position of the chief mechanical engineer on the Great Western. Until the end of Churchward's reign he was in no way subject to the general manager but answerable only to the chairman, and though the position was different for Collett he remained very much a power in the land, with the running department firmly under his control.

The position was very different on the LMS, and the Southern,

4–6–2 No 111 *The Great Bear* when new. The front footsteps were removed very soon after the locomotive went into service

where the running department was quite separate from the cme's domain, and headed by a superintendent of motive power, who on the LMS at least tended to regard the former's department as one to be viewed with deep suspicion, and harried or even bullied at times. E. S. Cox has written of one chief of motive power, J. E. Anderson, who 'chastised our department with whips', and his successor David Urie, who 'chastised us with scorpions'. On the Great Western the running superintendent was known as the outdoor assistant to the chief mechanical engineer, and was wholly subject to the latter.

To conclude our review of the 4-cylinder engines; as we have seen they had certain faults in design and practical disadvantages. On the other hand, their record in service was very fine as well as remarkably long. They and their direct descendants, the Stanier Princesses and Duchesses of the LMS, were by far the most successful 4-cylinder engines ever to run in this country. In the Duchesses the major design faults, the position of the cylinders and the inside valve gear were remedied, and a strong case can be made out for regarding them as the best British express locomotives ever built. Gresley fans would doubtless disagree strongly!

So much has been written about Britain's first Pacific, No 111 *The Great Bear*, with whole chapters devoted to it by Colonel Rogers in his biography of Churchward, and by O. S. Nock in his monograph on the Stars, Castles and Kings, that there is little that needs to be added. Many have asked why the engine was built, and two views have been put forward by various writers. Some believe that *The Great Bear* was built as cheaply as possible, using existing parts except for the boiler, purely for reasons of prestige, at the instigation of certain enthusiastic directors on the locomotive committee. The other view still more firmly held by other writers was that Churchward was looking to the future, and seeking far more power even than was provided by his Saints and Stars. It is known that he was very interested in the wide fireboxes becoming popular in the USA, and introduced into this country by Ivatt on the Great Northern Atlantics. My own belief is that, as so often in such controversies, both sides are right. If some of the directors wanted to be able to claim that the Great Western had by far the largest and most powerful engine in the country, Churchward may well have seized the opportunity both to satisfy their demands and try out a wide firebox with a view to future needs for still more power.

Four cylinder 4–6–0 No 6013 *King Henry VIII* outside 'A' shop at Swindon Works. It was typical of the class as built

10

Design faults and weaknesses

We have already expressed the opinion in Chapter 6 that Churchward was the greatest designer of locomotives this country has seen. He was an outstanding engineer and a great man. Like other men though he was not perfect. He had 'blind spots' which he never overcame, and he made mistakes, some of which he seemed strangely unwilling to put right. In general principles, planning a standard range, and in making big improvements in boilers, cylinders and valve motion, he excelled. It was mainly in frame design that he fell down badly.

On the Midland & South Western Junction Railway the soundest engines were ten Beyer Peacock 0–6–0s, which proved invaluable both for goods and passenger work. They were sturdy and reliable, and powerful within the limitations of their size and weight. Their frames however were light and not very deep. Every one had cracked at the centre horn gap, and they all had large patches riveted on at this point. For this reason, the general expectation was that the 'Western' would scrap the lot as soon as it took over. It did nothing of the kind. The 'Western' produced a new standard taper boiler, virtually Standard No 3 with a shorter firebox, specially for the MSWJR 19 class 0–6–0s and the Taff Vale A class 0–6–2 tanks. This boiler became the Standard 10, later used on the 2251 class 0–6–0s and the 9400 and 1500 class 0–6–0 pannier tanks.

A large number of these boilers was ordered from the Vulcan Foundry, and all ten MSWJR engines were taken to Swindon and rebuilt with them as quickly as possible. With an increase of pressure from 140lb/sq in to 165lb/sq in and the improved steaming capacity, these good engines became outstanding. The liveliest run I ever had on the MSW was behind one of them.

Swindon was not worried about their cracked frames, even when

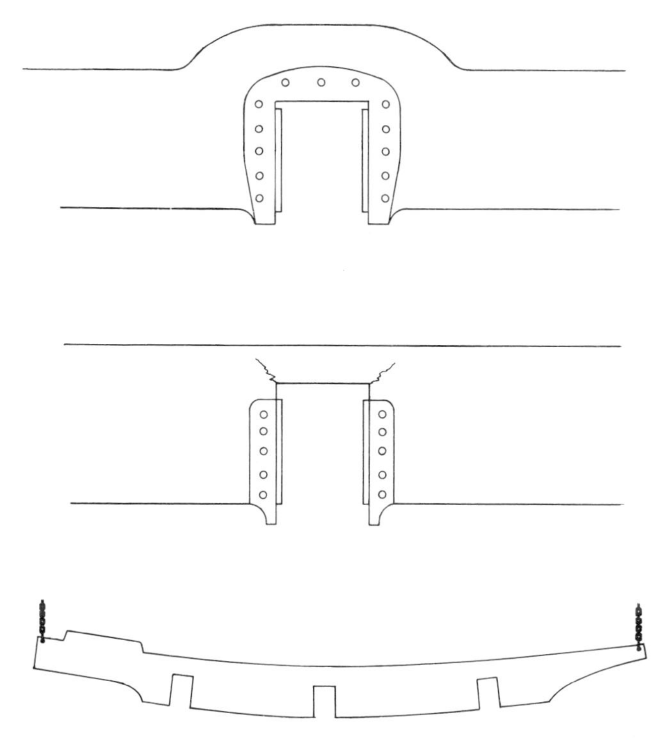

Main frame cracks: at the top the deeper frames and strength imparted by the horns around the cut-away compared with the GWR pattern in the centre. Bottom: the effect of lifting at the frame-ends

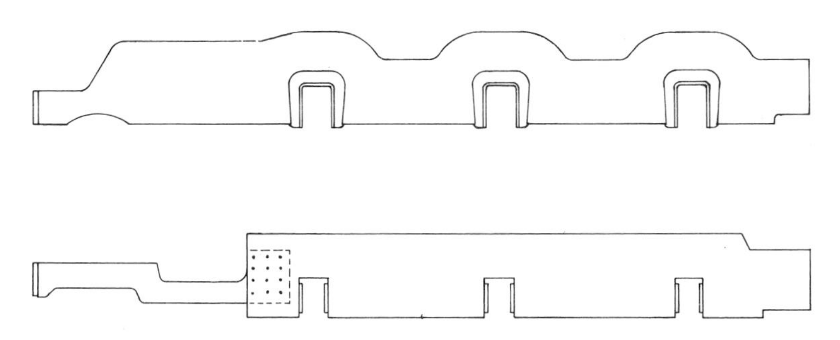

Comparison between one-piece frames used by other companies (top) and the frames used by the GWR with an extension frame shown for example for locomotives with 5ft 8in driving wheels — the 43xx 2–6–0s and the 2–6–2 tanks

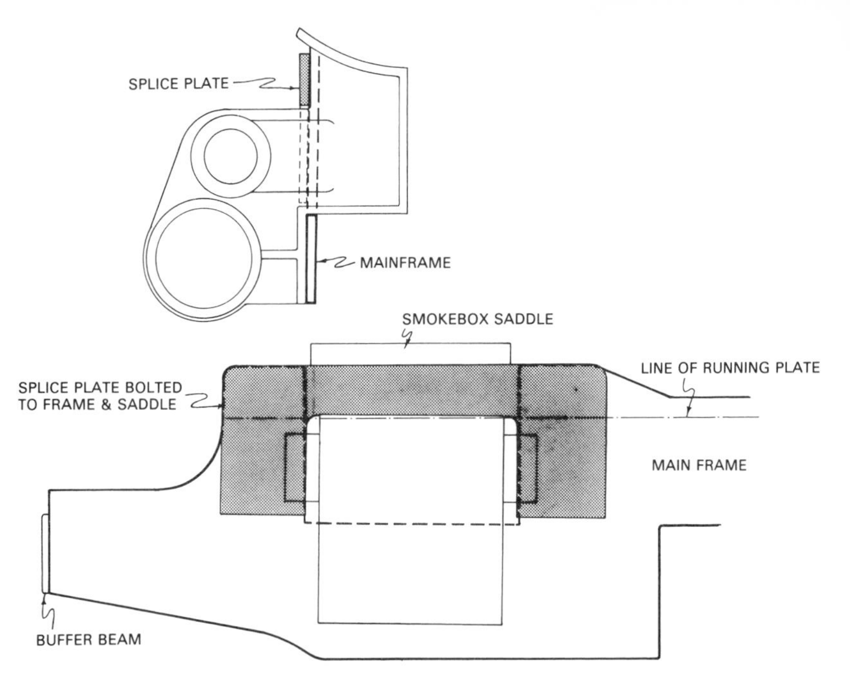

Drawing showing how the extension frames could have been eliminated by using splice plates as devised by Holcroft for three-cylinder 2–6–0s on the Southern Railway

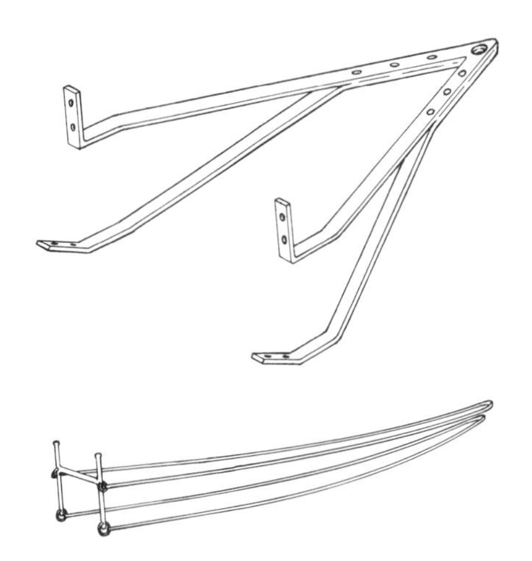

The reins for controlling the pony truck of engines with two-wheel trucks

increasing the load on them. Patching frames had become by then an old Wiltshire custom. I never remember seeing a locomotive frame at Swindon which was not welded and patched all over the place, except for old and small engines, and the Armstrong class double-framed 4–4–0s, which as pointed out in Chapter 4, had much better and stronger frames than any of their successors.

The reason for all these cracked frames was so simple and obvious that is is astonishing that no re-design seems ever to have been attempted. It was just bad design, a quite unnecessary and senseless departure from standard practice. The weakest points in any plate frame are the horn gaps. Normal British practice has been to carry the top line of the frame in a generous upward curve over the horn gaps, to provide depth of metal to compensate for what has been cut away. It was also normal practice to reinforce the frames at these points by using substantial horseshoe castings for the hornblocks, riveted (or on some of the BR standard engines, welded) to the frame plates. Churchward for some strange reason did neither of these things. All his frames had straight horizontal tops, providing no extra metal over the horns where it was needed. He made things worse by always using separate horn blocks, which did not support the frame at all. Most engineers often had to use the latter for trailing coupled wheels it is true, as there was seldom room for the horseshoe type under the firebox, but it is on the driving horn gap that the worst strain usually comes, and there is no need whatever to use separate horn blocks there.

I once tackled Holcroft on this matter. He seemed unable to see my point, saying that it was the business of the hornstays to provide the necessary strength and support. It is however notoriously difficult to get and maintain a perfect fit with hornstays. In any case the damage is usually done when the engine is lifted to remove or replace the wheels, and the hornstays have had to be removed. When the engine is lifted by cranes at the two ends with the hornstays off, there is a tremendous bending strain on the frames, and the bending naturally takes place at the weakest points, the horngaps, especially the ones near the middle. I have seen frames being lifted and taking up a clearly visible curve in the vertical plane. It is not surprising that such unsupported frames should crack at the top corners of the horngaps. They soon did, and had to be patched. Later on they were both welded and patched. I once mentioned the matter to Cecil J. Allen, who took it up with an engineer he knew at Swindon. The latter maintained that this design of frame and hornblocks was used to save weight, so as to allow the largest possible boiler. However, any weight thus saved must soon have been put back in patches.

What is extraordinary is that neither Churchward or his successors ever seem to have learned and modified the design. Stanier learned the lesson in the end, and used curved top frames and horseshoe castings on the largest LMS engines.

The various standard outside 2-cylinder engines, except for the later Halls built under Hawksworth and his County class 4–6–0s, all had another frame weakness. The plate frames ended behind the cylinders, and forged-steel 'extension frames' were bolted on to carry the combined cylinder and saddle castings and the buffer beams. They were used because Churchward seemed to be under the impression that it was impossible to use the American style cylinder and saddle castings with plate frames, so that these forgings in effect provided bar frame sections at the front. However, Gresley used massive one-piece castings comprising three cylinders with their steam chests and the saddle all in one with full length plate frames, on both his P2 2–8–2s and his V2 2–6–2s, showing that it could be done. He managed this by having a deeper slot between the outside cylinder and steam chest and the rest of the casting, into which the cut-away part of the frame could fit.

After Harold Holcroft had gone to the South Eastern & Chatham Railway, he was asked by R. E. L. Maunsell to design a 3-cylinder version of the N class 2–6–0s. He wished to use a two-piece casting for the three cylinders, with two cylinders in one piece, and one in the other. As he himself said, 'because of the trouble experienced with the extension frames' he did not use them. Instead he used a deep cut-out in the frames to take the cylinder castings, and a 'splice plate' bridging the gap just above the steamchest. These splice plates were bolted to the frames fore and aft of the cylinders, to the cylinder casting, and to the saddle casting, which in this design was separate. This made a very strong and rigid job, showing that the use of extension frames was not really necessary.

Other examples of poor design were the bar frame bogies and pony trucks. When the Cirencester Works of the Midland & South

Western Junction was closed its staff were moved to Swindon, except for a number who had already been sent to Worcester. The works there was a relic of the 'Old Worse & Worse', the one-time Oxford, Worcester & Wolverhampton Railway. It was a kind of 'torture chamber' for locomotives, where some incredibly bad practices were indulged with the connivance or even at the behest of the then divisional locomotive superintendent. His one idea seemed to be to rush the engines back into traffic, whether they were fit to run or not. But that is a story beyond the scope of this book.

When I was sent to Swindon, I was for my sins posted to Martin's gang in the 'A' erecting shop. Chargeman Martin was usually described by the men under him as 'an old woman'. He was a fussy little man with a spinsterish manner. Possibly because the chief foreman did not regard him very highly, we seemed to get all the worst jobs. For overhaul we mostly had double-framed Bulldogs, which were horrid to work on. After 55 years I still remember working, with a smoky paraffin flare lamp, with head and shoulders in the space of some 14in between inner and outer frames, with an inch thick layer of filthy black grease all round and above me.

We also had all the 'outstation' bogies and pony-trucks sent to us for repair. These had given trouble, been taken off at the sheds, and sent up to Swindon Works. They were nightmarish contraptions, so awkward and fiddly to repair that, being on piecework, we had not a hope of earning the usual bonus. They always took far more man-hours than they were supposed to.

As we saw in Chapter 6, when Churchward realised that it was essential to break right away from the old Victorian ideas he took contemporary American practice as his guide, generally speaking with excellent results. Unfortunately he copied some of the bad features as well as the good. One of the worst of these was the bar-frame bogie. This concept went back to very early days, about the 1840s, when industrialisation in the United States had not proceeded very far, and locomotives were designed which could be built and maintained largely by blacksmiths. Hence the use of wrought-iron bars bolted together, instead of pressed and machined plates and castings.

The Churchward bogie frame had as its principal member a rectangle of steel bars welded together, the bars being some 4in wide, but only 1½in thick. As the length of the frame was nearly 10ft, strength in a vertical direction was almost nil. To this rectangle short vertical bars were bolted to act as hornblocks. A very flimsy horizontal bar connected the four hornblocks on each side, and acted as a bottom frame member. These two bottom rails were joined to each other at the ends only, by two quite thin circular rods inside tubular distance-pieces. There were frail diagonal members, joining top and bottom rails, at the front only. The whole frame was almost unbelievably weak, a sort of outsize 'Meccano' joined together with nuts and bolts.

In theory this frame carried no weight, and its sole purpose was to hold the axleboxes in their correct positions both transversely and fore-and-aft. Weight was imposed on the buckles of the inverted springs, at first by a cross-member and sprink links, but later by the cross-member and the de Glehn side bearers. The spring on each side was inside a cradle, to which in turn it transferred the weight by short links. The ends of the cradles rested on the axleboxes and placed the weight on them.

Anyone who has ever had an old car knows that springs lose some of their strength and settle after a long period of service. This happened to the bogie springs after a high mileage. The axleboxes could then rise far enough in their guides to give the top frame member a series of smart clouts. Having no vertical strength, the frame promptly bent upwards. Swindon used to get quite a number of these bent frames to be rectified. One in particular I remember seeing when it arrived. It was bent like a bow. The ends must have been two or three inches above the centre and at an angle. This must have forced the axlebox guides out of position, and displaced them from the vertical. Why no serious accident had been caused was a mystery. My guess is that the engine did de-rail, but in shed precincts, so no great harm was done. In less serious cases the displaced horns caused the axleboxes to run hot, and the engine to be stopped before anything worse happened. Years later I mentioned these problems to Harold Holcroft, who seemed very surprised. The drawing office just did not seem to know of the troubles its designs were causing. Either no-one dared tell those responsible, or they just did not want to know.

For the Castles and Halls Collett did strengthen the bogie frame somewhat with heavier sections, separate stout hornstays, and stronger diagonals, but he kept the basic design. It was very unfortunate that this bogie was so unsound structurally, as in other respects it was very good indeed. Its 7ft wheelbase, the excellent Adams arrangement of inverted springs and equalising cradles, and good spring control of sideplay, provided smooth running and excellent guidance, while the widely spaced side-bearers checked any tendency for the engine to roll.

When Hawksworth became chief mechanical engineer, he provided a plate frame bogie for the 6959 series of Halls, and the County class 4–6–0s. Unfortunately he gave up the excellent Adams springing system in favour of an individual plate spring for each wheel. These springs were short and stiff, and could not provide anything like such good riding. In one way and another the Great Western never did have the outstandingly good bogies it could have had if only strong plate frames had been combined with the Adams springing, the de Glehn bearers and side control. Stanier used similar bar frame bogies on all his Pacifics, but they were of much heavier and more substantial construction, with strong diagonal bracing. These seem to have given satisfactory service, but he used plate frames on all his 4–6–0s.

The pony trucks were if anything worse, and when I was at Swindon we had a large number in for repair, especially from the small 4500 class 2–6–2 tanks, which had two to each engine, unlike the large 2–6–2Ts which had a sturdy radial axlebox arrangement at the rear, and just one pony truck in front. These trucks were somewhat similar in construction to the bogies, being made up of short pieces of bar joined together with nuts and bolts. As the longest of the bars was only 2ft long, with very little of its length unsupported, there was not the bending trouble we had with the bogie frames. The main weakness was with the 'reins' — yes, 'reins to control the pony'. One pictures an American farmer of the days of Abraham Lincoln driving his buggy to market, and of course using reins to manage his pony! All pony trucks on locomotives have to be anchored to a pin fixed to the frame several feet to the rear (in the case of a leading truck), to control the swing. On other British Railways the controlling arm usually consisted of a very substantial triangular girder, with the sides of angle steel. The short side of this isosceles triangle would be bolted or riveted to the back of the truck frame, and at the apex the metal would be thickened to provide a deep and substantial boss with a hole for the pivot pin, which was secured to a frame cross-member. This triangular member was usually built up by welding; in later practice it could be a steel casting. Such a triangular girder, of adequate section and with straight sides, is of course a very strong and rigid structure.

The reins used on GWR pony trucks were by comparison very flimsy, and since the members were not straight but contained several bends the structure was not inherently rigid. On the small 2–6–2 tanks, the reins consisted of four steel strips 4in wide, but no more than 1in thick. The two top members were bent sharply upwards through more than a right-angle at the front end to form a 'tab' bolted to the rear vertical frame members, which acted as the back horn-blocks. The lower members were almost straight at the ends, and only had to be very slightly bent where they were bolted to a horizontal truck frame member. All four strips were bent through various angles, inwards and upwards, until they were united by rivetting in front of an eye for the pivot. On the larger 2–6–2 tanks, 2–8–0s, 2–6–0s, and 2–8–0 tanks, these reins were of somewhat stouter metal but were still not very rigid. In service the quite thin bent strips became distorted, often with the bends tending to straighten, which is what one would expect. A triangle is a naturally rigid structure only if the sides are straight.

We used to get many of these pony trucks whose reins needed to be restored to their proper shape and length, because any straightening of the bends made them longer. To get them right they had to be made to fit a jig provided for the purpose, a quite large and cumbersome structure welded up from steel tube, strip and angle. To get the reins to the exact curvature needed for the assembly to fit the jig usually required dismantling, attention by the blacksmiths, and re-assembling two or three times. It was a procedure very wasteful and expensive in man-hours, and could so easily have been avoided by better design. Why the distortion of the reins in service did not cause accidents is something of a mystery. I think there were a few derailments almost certainly due to this cause, but not nearly so many as might have been expected, considering the number of pony trucks sent to us to be put right.

With the building of the 4575 series of small 2–6–2 tanks in 1927, strengthening brackets were inserted between the top and bottom rein members on each side about the middle of their length. These would appreciably have increased the rigidity of the arrangement but were definitely not in use before.

The other faults which require mention concern footplate arrangements, where the work of drivers and firemen was made unnecessarily hard, and the protection given them was rather scanty. I have already mentioned in Chapter 5 the wide use of a reversing lever on all goods, mixed-traffic and tank engines, and Churchward's earlier express engines as well, instead of the excellent screw gear devised in Dean's time. This was extraordinary, and seems to have been part of Churchward's obsession with things American, for in the early 1900s reversing levers, known there for some obscure reason as 'Johnson Bars', were still almost universal even on such big engines as the earliest articulated Mallets. Churchward adopted the American Norris lever, with two catches one on each side, engaging with staggered notches in the two quadrants but both raised by one trigger, to permit smaller changes in the cut-off. However, it needed an exceptionally strong man or a very rash one to disengage the catch and try to adjust the cut-off at speed. The lever could all too easily be torn from the driver's grasp and the engine fly into full gear, causing much of the fire to be thrown out of the chimney, and probably violent slipping as well. If on the other hand the driver clung bravely to the lever he might be thrown about and injured. These engines had therefore to be driven on the regulator willy-nilly, and this device for making fine adjustments of cut-off possible was just a waste of effort.

At one time I made fairly frequent journeys between Maidenhead and Paddington, at first behind 4–4–2 County tanks, and later with 61xx 2–6–2 engines. The latter in particular were splendid engines for the work, except for this one detail. It was very noticeable that the acceleration after every stop was in two or three bursts, with brief pauses as the driver shut-off steam to move the lever and shorten the cut-off. Screw reverse would have been so much better.

Collett improved things a little by fitting screw reverse to the last batch of 2–6–0s in the 93xx series, some of the small tank engines used for auto-train working, and all his mixed-traffic 4–6–0s, (Halls, Granges and Manors) also to most though not all of his 2251 class

0–6–0s. However, all his additions to the 2–8–0 tender engines retained the lever. This must have made the handling of long loose-coupled goods trains for which these engines were designed very difficult over varying gradients, for the utmost delicacy of handling was needed to avoid the risk of parting the train. Here again, the smooth adjustment of cut-off possible with a screw would have been far better.

When Churchward did fit a reversing screw, he placed it right back in the cab, so that it took up all the room where the driver needed to stand to look out comfortably, whether through the front window or leaning over the side. The driver had perforce to lean over the reverser to see where he was going, and this produced a curvature of the spine which became known as 'the 29 bend'. It also forced the driver's legs uncomfortably near the heat from the firehole. It was only with some, though not all, of the Princess batch of Stars, that the screw was moved forward into a kind of cubby-hole protruding from the cab front. Curiously enough the final batch, the Abbeys, reverted to the old bad arrangement. I have seen photographs of one or two of them provided with a cubby-hole, and the gear moved out of the way. Whether these were exceptions when built or had been altered subsequently, I do not know. All Collett's and Hawksworth's 4–6–0s had the screw forward in a cubby-hole, so that the driver could stand or sit on a spartan tip-up seat, squarely in front of his window.

In other respects the arrangement of controls was better than many, though as engines and boilers got bigger the vacuum brake handle became very high and further from the cab side. At least the sand levers were not placed on the fireman's side, out of reach of the driver, as was often done elsewhere. Churchward's cabs were scanty by modern ideas, but about average by the standards of 1902 when they were designed, and they gave much better shelter than for instance the terribly skimpy affairs on the Dean Goods. In fairness to Churchward, he did try a large double side-window cab on the Badminton class 4–4–0 No 3297 *Earl Cawdor*, when in 1903 he rebuilt this engine with a large round-topped boiler as an experiment. The men raised such strong objections that the standard cab was very soon put back, even before the non-standard boiler was replaced by a normal taper boiler. Presumably the enginemen felt too

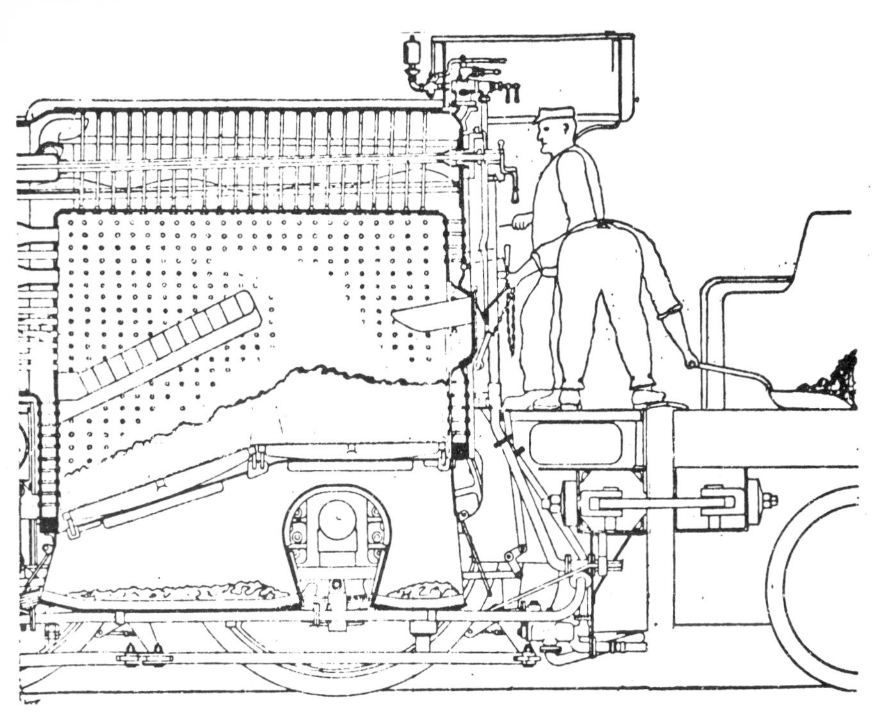

The back-breaking job of the fireman with the high footplate of the Churchward engine coupled to low tenders. (*Courtesy Allen & Unwin*)

shut in, and found the extended roof got in the way when raking or dropping the fire. Anyway, Churchward could hardly be blamed after that for not bothering to give better shelter.

However, in the 1920s when I worked on the Great Western, nearly all engines with open cabs, whether tender or tank, carried a rolled-up tarpaulin sheet secured to the back of the cab roof, which could be unrolled and tied by the bottom corners to the tender hand-rails when it was necessary to run backwards or stand for some time in rain or snow. Side doors between engine and tender were fitted to the pioneer 2–8–0 No 97 when first built, and possibly to a few other engines around 1903. They were soon removed, and no other Great Western tender engines ever had them, though all the later tank engines did. With the constant movement between engine and tender, such doors must have been very prone to rattle; most Scottish engines had them from about 1890, and all the other British railways adopted them from about 1912 to 1926. They were needed to stop draughts, particularly in strong side-winds, and were a valuable safeguard against men being thrown off.

A very good feature of Churchward's cabs was that the roof was made of two skins of tongued and grooved wooden strips, covered with roofing felt. They must have greatly reduced the noise on the footplate, and made the cab cooler in summer and perhaps a little warmer in winter. They were doubtless an expensive luxury, and a start seems to have been made during the first world war to replace them with cheaper, and noisy, sheet metal. All had gone by 1925, or so it appeared when I went to Swindon.

Perhaps the biggest drawback from the men's point of view was the continued use of Dean pattern tenders, with just the addition of water pick-up gear, and the replacement of coal rails by sheet steel fenders. These tenders were long and low and were not too bad in Victorian times, when runs were shorter, loads and therefore coal consumption were smaller, and cab floors were only the thickness of the wood above running plate level. Churchward's bigger engines however had the cab floor raised by some 18in or more above the tender floor level.

The wretched fireman therefore had to bend double to dig up every shovel-full of coal from the level of his feet or even lower. These tenders were in no way self-trimming, so that on a long run the fireman had to keep going back into the tender to bring coal forward. The continued use of such tenders on big engines, including even the early Castles, and on the longest non-stop run in Great Britain, (at one time in the world) was nothing less than cruelty to firemen. How the men survived, particularly on the Cornish Riviera Express with its 225 miles non-stop from London to Plymouth, without going sick with serious back trouble, is a marvel.

The Collett tenders, introduced for the Kings in 1927, were distinctly better, but it was not until 1946 that the Great Western had any really civilised tenders, with cupboards and proper coal gates, when the Hawksworth pattern appeared on the 1000 class Counties and the last batches of Castles.

11

Collett and the Crisis in Wales

H. A. V. Bulleid in his outstandingly good book *Master Builders of Steam* referred to what he called 'The deplorable railway habit of promotion by seniority'. C. B. Collett was certainly the senior man in the locomotive, carriage & wagon department, and as assistant chief mechanical engineer would naturally expect to succeed Churchward.

The directors however might have done a good deal better to have ignored protocol and looked further for their next CME. As we have already said, Collett was a very capable works and production engineer. He had been an excellent works manager for a number of years, but with the increasing importance of industrial relations after the first world war it is doubtful if he would still have been successful if he had continued in that capacity. He had the reputation of being a difficult man to work with. He was devious, narrow in his outlook, and could be secretive and unreasonable. He discouraged his staff from associating with engineers from other companies, and actually forbade them to join the Institution of Locomotive Engineers. He was widely mistrusted and disliked, and was not the man to lead and inspire a team, a role in which Churchward had excelled.

Churchward and his team had put Great Western practice years ahead of everyone else. With Collett being neither a locomotive designer himself nor one to encourage his subordinates to take an initiative, design just stagnated, and towards the end of its existence the Great Western became 'a tail-end Charlie' where progress was concerned. Fortunately Churchward's standard designs were so good that this was not nearly so harmful as it might have been.

With hindsight, the company would probably have done much better to have appointed Stanier, who was next in succession and only five years younger than Collett. Stanier was a much more broad-minded and enterprising engineer, always willing to learn. He was extremely good in human relationships, well-liked by all ranks in the company's service. However it was not to be, and the GWR's loss was the LMSR's gain, and the latter's need was immeasurably greater. They had had no Churchward.

Collett's first effort in producing a new design was the famous Castle, which we have already dealt with in Chapter 9. It was as we have seen just a slight enlargement of Churchward's Star, with nothing new about it at all except the cab. Its performance, aided by excellent Welsh steam coal and the very fine footplate traditions inherited from Churchward, gained Collett a fame and reputation which he had done little to earn. We must not be too critical though, and he did from time to time have bright ideas. For instance, the decision which he seems to have made himself without consulting anyone, to give the Kings trailing springs with thinner plates but half as many again, was very successful indeed. It transformed the riding of the Kings, and I believe that similar more flexible springs were afterwards widely used on other types when the use of equalising levers to coupled wheels was discontinued from 1927 onwards.

On the production side in which his true gifts lay Collett made notable improvements, especially the introduction of Zeiss optical apparatus for lining-up frames, cylinders, horns, and slide-bars, a huge improvement on the 'stick and string' methods traditionally used from the days of Gooch and Stephenson. Thus it was possible to assemble engines with far greater accuracy than ever before, making for smooth running, less friction and longer life. The tendency of most classes of locomotive to include a few 'black sheep' with performance well below average, was probably due more to slight inaccuracies in assembly than anything else. When I was at Swindon there was a strong tradition that *The Great Bear* was just such a rogue engine, not too well put together in the first place, and therefore unable to do justice to the design. *The Great Bear* was said to retain the same character and reputation after being rebuilt as a Castle in 1924, well before the introduction of optical alignment, which was first used in the batch of Castles built in 1934. Incidentally, the next ten after these, Nos 5031–40, had the reputation of being the best batch of the class ever built. Certainly some of the finest Castle runs ever recorded were made by engines of this series, including the fastest run ever, (until deliberately eased down) on the Cheltenham Flyer, by No 5039 *Rhuddlan Castle*.

The next design to be produced under Collett was the 56xx class 0–6–2 tank engine for South Wales. This was Collett's first and last attempt to do anything new and original. We now have a piece of engineering scandal to relate which hardly anyone seems to know about, as there was a cover-up operation reminiscent of the American 'Watergate' except that the Swindon one succeeded. I venture to suggest that President Nixon would have kept his job if he had been given the advantage of Swindon training!

To understand what happened we must first look at the Grouping of the railways, authorised by Act of Parliament in 1919, and which took effect in 1922–3. Before then there had been more than 50 separate companies owning and running standard gauge lines. They varied in size from the Easingwold Railway in Yorkshire with six route miles and two locomotives, to the three giants, the Great Western, the Midland and the London & North Western.

Under the Act, these varied and numerous railway companies were mostly incorporated into the 'big four' by amalgamation or take-over. Unlike the other three new companies in which large or medium sized railways were amalgamated and new institutions with fresh names emerged, the Great Western simply swallowed a number of small companies, and retained its name and identity. Apart from three small lines in England, of which the Midland & South Western Junction was the largest with 63 route miles and 29 locomotives, all the lines taken-over were in Wales. Except for the Cambrian, a poverty-stricken stretched-out line threading through the mountains of Central Wales, all these railways were short, most connecting coal mines with seaports. Though short, they carried very heavy traffic in those days. The largest, the Taff Vale, had a four-track main line which was hardly adequate for the traffic, and it had been the best-paying railway in Britain.

Now these smaller lines had no love for the 'Western', (it was never spoken or thought of as 'Great'). It was the enemy, the big bully next door. For the Great Western not only ran rival branches up the same valleys in many cases, it creamed-off all the long-distance traffic which had originated on the Welsh lines. They were in fact to a considerable extent feeders for the GWR.

When the Welsh companies learned that in two or three years time they would be compulsorily absorbed by the Great Western they did not see any advantage in repairing and overhauling locomotives which would soon be the property and the headaches of 'big brother'. In most cases they just didn't — they ran them into the ground. There was one honourable exception, the Rhymney Railway, which had built itself a fine new works at Caerphilly about the turn of the century. The Rhymney was justly proud of it and continued to make good use of the works. In England the MSWJR had maintained its engines better than anyone, as the Great Western authorities testified.

In South Wales though the GWR inherited a desperate situation. The coal and steel traffic was still immense, and there were simply not enough engines in a fit state to do the work. Drastic steps had to be and were taken. Scrapping of old engines, already delayed by the first world war, was virtually forbidden, and many odd types and 'one-offs' were expensively rebuilt and re-boilered, some to last only four or five years. The building of Castles was slowed down, so that the first 20 took three years to produce. The building of 43xx class 2–6–0s was taken away from Swindon and contracted to Robert Stephenson & Co, the first time that the GWR had gone to an outside builder for 60 years, since Armstrong's time.

When I arrived at Swindon more than two years after the take-over, the place was cluttered up with stripped-down wrecks from South Wales awaiting new boilers and other major components. Many of them were the Taff Vale A class 0–6–2 tanks, the newest design in Wales, all built within the previous four to ten years. This shows how they had been abused and neglected. To speed up things, new taper boilers were ordered in quantity from the Vulcan Foundry and Stephenson.

At first new work at Swindon was largely concentrated on the 52xx series of 2–8–0 tanks, which had been specially evolved for South Wales mineral traffic. These were not at all popular with the Welshmen, who claimed that they were too long for their turn-outs and too wide for their platforms — they much preferred the 0–6–2 tanks to which they were accustomed.

Collett had to think again quickly. He gave orders for a new design of 0–6–2T to be rushed out, and rushed out they were. The working drawings were dated August 1924, and the first engine steamed in December. The drawing office worked much overtime, and the works literally operated night and day. There was then a regular night shift, with its own foreman. The number of gangs in the erecting shop on new work was raised from the usual four to five.

The wheelbase and general proportions of the new engines were taken from the Rhymney R class, usually considered the best of the many and varied Welsh 0–6–2T designs. The Standard No 2 taper boiler was to be used. Side tanks, cab and bunker were taken straight from the 2–8–0 tanks. Pistons 18in diameter were a standard size, as were the 8in piston valves, the same diameter as in Stars and Castles. The only major new parts required were the cylinder castings, so it seemed as though there would be no difficulty in producing a successful machine in a very short time. It was intended to have valve motion and events as in the standard outside-cylinder classes. As the Stephenson valve gear on these was inside anyway, it seemed a simple matter to use it with inside cylinders; it may well be that with all the pressure on the drawing office at the time, the drawing out of the gear was given to a junior draughtsman.

A first batch of 50 of this untried design was laid down, and the work was pressed forward so vigorously that the first engine was ready for trials in four months, just before Christmas 1924. We can imagine the excitement. The new work pits were at the furthest north-west corner of the 'A' Shop. Pulled onto the traverser by capstan, the engine would have been moved sideways between the lines of pits, out through big sliding doors in the wall next to the main line, onto a siding which ran along outside the wall. Quite a long, triumphal ride through groups of interested workmen. Once outside, the works pilot, at that time probably No 843, former MSWJR 0–6–0T No 14, would be attached to pull the new engine to the steaming pits. These radiated from a turntable in the space between 'A' Shop and the old part of the works.

The fire lit and steam raised, everything most carefully oiled and checked over, all was ready for the trial trip. A driver and fireman from the running shed would have come over, and the chargeman and an apprentice from the erecting gang would be ready to ride. On this special occasion Ted Plaister would probably have come to watch. He was chief foreman of 'A' Shop, with 3,000 men under him,

Collett 56xx class 0–6–2 tank No 5619 for South Wales. The large reversing lever and tool boxes are prominent in the cab

a great potentate. A representative of the drawing office, and the works manager or his assistant, might well have come to see the first trials of the new prototype.

Full forward gear, drain cocks open, lubricator set to give a generous flow of oil, a touch on the whistle, the regulator opened carefully, the engine moved forward a few yards. Then horrors! With fearful groans and screeches from underneath, two of the four beats virtually disappeared. The regulator was shut hastily, and Swindon's fine new engine shuddered to a shrieking halt. Imagine the consternation. Swindon at that time thought that it was infallible. Other lines might have such failures, but not 'God's Wonderful Railway'. Forty-nine similar engines were on order, twelve at least being erected, two or three almost ready for trials. All were desperately needed.

To understand what had happened it is best to refer to the drawing of the standard Stephenson valve gear on page 71. There it will be seen that the extension rod, connecting the die block with the inner rocker arm, is inclined at a steep angle because of the vertical distance, about 18in, between the centre lines of piston and valve rods. On the 4–6–0s the angle is about 12°, but on the smaller engines it is around 22°. This naturally causes considerable up-thrust, which would be worse when everything was new and stiff. Now the rock-shafts on the outside cylinder engines were massive affairs, running in substantial bearings 10in long and 5in diameter. These could take any amount of up-thrust. The junior draughtsman whom we assume to have drawn out the gear for the 0–6–2Ts would have found no rock-shaft to connect the upper end of the extension rod. However, in much the same relative position was the end of the valve spindle, so he connected it to that, with a simple fork and pin joint. The end of the valve spindle was unsupported in any way. When the engine started to move, the thrust just caused it to bend upwards. The groans were the result of the bent spindle binding in the stuffing box. Bending the spindle inevitably shortened it, bringing the piston valve too far back to open the front ports properly; hence the two very feeble beats.

Simple and obvious, the trouble should have been foreseen and guarded against by providing a substantial guide for the valve spindle. The blame really rested with Collett himself. Churchward would have spotted the weakness before initialling the drawing and letting it pass to the shops. But Collett was no Churchward, and may not even have checked the drawing, but left it to the chief draughtsman who was also to blame anyway for not exercising closer supervision. In fairness it must be pointed out that the pressure on the drawing office at this time must have been almost intolerable. In addition to the ordinary work, there was the immense task of trying to adapt hundreds of absorbed engines to take Great Western boilers and other standard fittings. The rush job on the 0–6–2Ts must have been the final straw.

What was to be done? Collett was in a very difficult position. He had only succeeded the great and universally admired Churchward about two years before. He was widely disliked and mistrusted. This was his first and last attempt at producing anything original. All the

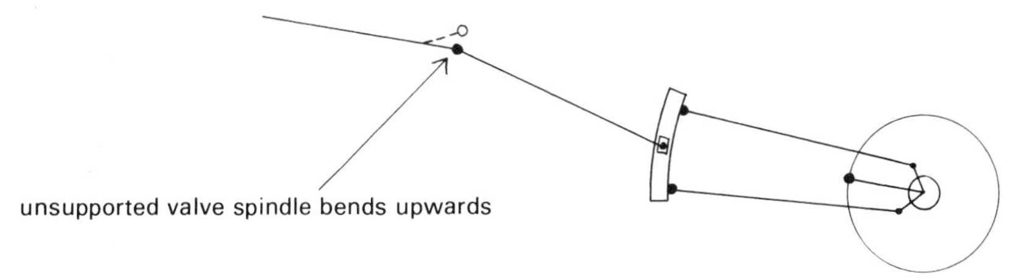

The unsupported valve spindle arrangement on the first 56xx 0–6–2T, showing why it bent upwards

other designs for which he was responsible were straightforward enlargements or slight modifications of engines produced by Churchward, Dean or even the Armstrongs. His first four or five Castles were running and doing well, but they were basically Churchward Stars with a few inches added here and there, and a larger and better cab.

Though no engine designer, Collett was an able administrator. He was also a very cunning and determined man, with a knack of getting his own way. He seems to have issued two commands, probably the next day, after a few hours to think over the problem. One was that the responsible staff of the section in the drawing office were not to leave their boards and go home until they had worked out a solution. The other order was, 'This thing has not happened. Anyone who dares to say it has will be dismissed instantly'.

The drawing office not surprisingly over-reacted. From providing no support for the valve spindles at all, it swung to the opposite extreme, providing a massive cross-member bridging the frames immediately over the valve spindle ends. To the latter were fitted miniature 3-bar crossheads, working in suitable guides bolted underneath the cross-member. While working on the rough draft of this chapter, I had a stroke of luck. Looking through J. H. Russell's *Pictorial History of Great Western Engines*, I discovered a rather faint but legible copy of the works drawing of the amended valve gear. It shows obvious signs of hasty improvisation. Instead of the steel casting which would normally be used for a frame cross-member, there are two lengths cut from a standard steel channel section such as might be used in a footbridge or a signal gentry. Some borrowing from the department next door seems to have taken place. One section of trough was inverted, and the two were placed back to back to form an improvised H-section girder. The troughs were not even rivetted together, but fastened with nuts and bolts. A rushed job if ever there was one, and it made the valve motion very inaccessible.

Interestingly enough, this drawing is dated August 1924, the same date as the original drawings, although the weakness was not discovered until mid-December! Clearly, as part of the 'cover-up', the original drawings were called in and burned, and the date faked on the new ones. The efforts to hide the horrid truth were remarkably successful. Face had to be saved, and it was. No-one seems to have been sacked. For one thing those in authority were really to blame. For another, if anyone concerned had ceased to work for the GWR there would have been no way to stop him talking. As it was Collett got away with his 'This thing did not happen' ploy remarkably well.

Of course rumours got around. The population of Swindon at that time was around 50,000 and about 17,000, nearly all men in those days, were employed by the Great Western, the vast majority in the works — most of the working population in fact, except for the necessary doctors, dentists, shopkeepers and the like (and, oh! ministers and parsons). Anything that happened in the works was of major interest in the town. But for many years afterwards, if any person of any standing on the railway was asked about these rumours, he would either deny that there was any trouble or say that he knew nothing about it. There is one very cautious and veiled reference to the incident, in K. J. Cook's very interesting book *Swindon Steam* which was not published until 1974, just 50 years after the event. Cook says there was some trouble with the valve-setting going awry on 'a few of the class' in their early days. This he attributes to distortion in the cylinder castings. Either Mr Cook was being very discreet or his memory had faded with the passing of years.

Readers may well be wondering how since the secret was so well kept I came to know so much about it. A few months after that disastrous trial trip, I went to lodge at a hostel in Old Swindon, where beside young clerks, budding auctioneers and the like, four or five Works premium apprentices were living. One, Hurry Riches, was the son of the last locomotive superintendent of the Rhymney Railway. His father had only resigned when the then recent takeover occurred. His grandfather, Tom Hurry Riches, had been a noted engineer in his day. For 40 years he was locomotive, carriage & wagon superintendent of the largest railway in Wales, the Taff Vale, and he was at one time president of the Institution of Mechanical Engineers.

Young Hurry Riches, thus 'born to the purple', was a privileged person, and was allotted to a 'new work' gang. Obviously with around 60 or 70 engines built new each year and some 1,800 given a thorough overhaul, nice clean jobs on new work were scarce. The vast majority had to be content with the filthy and less exciting tasks of stripping-down and patching-up older engines. Anyway, Hurry Riches was working for a long period on building 56xx class engines and he was present when the hiatus happened. He told me all about it. So far as I remember he swore me to secrecy, but now that all those responsible are dead there can be no harm in telling the truth of what happened.

The 56xx class, carried on with the 66xx series, soon numbered 200 engines, 150 built at Swindon, the remaining 50 by Armstrong-Whitworth. They seem to have done their work reasonably well, and lasted almost to the end of steam; it seems as if there was some difficulty in finding suitable work for them towards the end, judging by the way they began to be scattered around the system in twos and threes, attached to such sheds as Leamington Spa and Slough. With their modern ports and valve gear, they had a good turn of speed for 4ft 7in driving wheels, and they were powerful, with a tractive effort of nearly 26,000lb. This last was a source of trouble. As so often happened with high-powered inside-cylinder engines (the LNER J39 0–6–0s and the LMS Class 7F 0–8–0s were other examples), the driving axleboxes wore very rapidly. There were two reasons why this was inevitable. The bearings of the outside-cylinder GWR engines were 10in long. On the 56xx class there was only room for 7in between the wheel and the crank web. Not only were the bearings little more than half the area, but with inside and outside cranks set at 180° the fore-and-aft thrust on the axleboxes is greatly increased. Connecting and coupling rods are pulling in opposite directions, and all the force of this reversal has to be taken by the driving axleboxes, which are well suited to cope with vertical loads, but very ill-adapted to near-horizontal thrusts.

In an attempt to reduce this heavy wear, which greatly reduced the mileage run between shoppings and so was very costly, a number of the class were after a time altered to have the Stroudley arrangement of cranks. In this the inside and outside cranks are in phase instead of opposite each other. It reduces the thrust by about half and so lessens wear, but since both cranks, big-end and coupling rod are on the same side, instead of largely balancing out, the balance weights have to be so large that they are difficult to accommodate in small wheels. They add very considerably to an already heavy axle load, and this is made more serious by the fact that this extra weight is unsprung. It is interesting to note that the Atbaras of 1900 and possibly some Bulldogs of the same period were built with the Stroudley crank arrangement, but they did not keep it for very long. On a recent visit to the Great Western Society Depot at Didcot I was able to inspect No 6697, one of the later batch built by Armstrong Whitworth. Mounting the front step and peering under the boiler, I was very interested to see in place of the improvised bolted channels for supporting the valve spindle guides a neat purpose-built cross-member in one piece. It could have been a steel casting, but looked more like a steel pressing. It seems likely that only the original 50 engines had the crude arrangement, though the improved form may have been special to Armstrong Whitworth.

The irony was that by the time the whole two hundred 56xx class had been completed and very many of the Welsh engines had been rebuilt, the bottom had begun to drop out of the Welsh coal trade, especially export business. This was partly due to loss of markets during the prolonged coal strike of 1926, but mainly to the change-over from coal to oil firing in ships, and later on to diesel engines. The huge expenditure on providing motive power for South Wales gave little financial return, but it is difficult to see how it could have been avoided. No one could have foreseen the decline in the coal trade — the shortage of engines was desperate for a time and had to be remedied.

12

Finale under Collett and Hawksworth

The Kings appeared in 1927, but it seems that the inspiration for them came from the general manager, Sir Felix Pole, rather than Collett. On his record, it is unlikely that the latter would have shown such boldness and enterprise without a very firm push. Sir Felix is said to have insisted on a tractive effort of not less than 40,000lb purely for reasons of publicity and prestige, hardly the best criterion for sound and practical design. To reach this figure, steam pressure was increased from the usual 225lb/sq in to 250lb/sq in and the stroke from 26in to 28in, both very good moves. They were not though sufficient to reach Pole's target, although the resultant tractive effort of nearly 39,000lb would have been more than adequate in service. So two fiddling little changes had to be made. A new size of driving wheel, 6ft 6in, was an expensive alteration, needing new patterns as well as a new tyre size; boring out the cylinder castings to 16¼in just shortened their lives. It is believed that all except the first five (some say all except No 6000 *King George V* itself) were turned out with 16in cylinders from the start, and nothing published about the resultant drop just below 40,000lb. The general manager and the publicity department had been appeased, and a return to commonsense could be made.

Considerable ingenuity was needed to design an engine of such power within strict weight limits (although these were in fact exceeded) and the loading gauge, while retaining the 4–6–0 chassis and the basic Star layout. The main responsibility for the design seems to have been taken by F. W. Hawksworth, by that time chief draughtsman. This was a big change from the previous régime, where design was inspired and to a considerable extent supervised by Churchward in person, leaving the chief draughtsman mainly as an administrator. As Holcroft has put it, the chief draughtsman (then

G. H. Burrows) spent most of the time in his office 'busy with staff matters and correspondence'. Now with a chief mechanical engineer taking little personal part in design which was not his métier, Hawksworth came into his own, and was in fact what his title suggests.

Had the general manager been in less of a hurry to have once again 'the most powerful locomotive in Britain', (although tractive effort is not a true criterion of power), and had Collett and Hawksworth been less frightened of any departure from what Churchward had done, there was a strong case for designing the new large engine from first principles instead of just enlarging the Star a little further. The King boiler, a proportionate enlargement of the excellent No 1, proved very successful and could hardly have been bettered except by providing a larger superheater from the start, instead of many years later. Better placing of the cylinders, and putting the valve gear outside, would surely have been very well worth while. The fact is that Churchward had rescued locomotive design from its Victorian groove in a brilliant way. After his retirement his successors let it slip back into an Edwardian groove, for by King Edward's death in 1910 Churchward's pioneering work was near its fulfilment. Design remained firmly in that groove, with some minor improvements under Hawksworth and Smeddle, not only to nationalisation but even after. Churchward's work however had been so sound and so far ahead of its time that this did not prove a disaster. By slight and usually unnecessary modifications to Churchward's standard designs, an excellent stud of engines for the vast majority of duties was maintained. It was only in providing top rank express locomotives, and easing the task of the enginemen, that something better could and should have been done.

After building 30 Kings, Collett contented himself with modifying his predecessors' designs, and building many more Castles. The continued production of the latter rather than more Kings has led some commentators to suggest that the latter were unsuccessful. This was not the case. The Kings were very good at their job, which was hauling the heaviest expresses over the routes on which their weight was allowed, to Plymouth via Westbury or Bristol, and to Wolverhampton via Bicester. Thirty engines were quite sufficient for these duties. A case could have been made for using them on the heavy

No 1026 *County of Salop*, the final development by Hawksworth of the classic Churchward two-cylinder 4–6–0. (*A. R. Brown*)

South Wales trains, with the laborious climb from the depths of the Severn Tunnel up onto the Cotswolds. If they had been so used another 10 or 15 might have been needed, but they never were during the lifetime of the company. Presumably the civil engineer would not allow them into South Wales. After the Kings were beginning to be displaced on the Plymouth route by diesels some of them were, though, stationed at Canton shed in Cardiff. Under nationalisation with a mechanical engineer, Robin Riddles, on the British Railways Board, but no civil engineer, the long dominance of the latter profession seemed to wither away, judging by what happened on the Liverpool Street to Cambridge line, where there had previously been very severe weight restrictions. After nationalisation the 93-ton Britannias, 2-cylinder engines at that, were simply introduced and often ran at very high speeds. Although I lived near the line at Sawbridgeworth at that time, I saw no signs of track or bridges being strengthened. Much of the Up line it is true had been relaid with heavier flat-bottom rail, but the Down line retained the old bull-head chaired track.

With the decline in the influence of the civil engineer, the Kings may well have been permitted in Wales without any up-grading of the track and bridges. There were however only about two years after their arrival at Canton before they were all withdrawn in 1962.

After the completion of the last of the 30 Kings in 1930, all that Collett ever did was to tinker around with his predecessors' designs. Some of this could be described as 'messing about' with them. Churchward as we have seen had very sensibly kept to only three wheel sizes, for goods, mixed-traffic and express service.

Collett proceeded to vary these standard diameters by small amounts of two or three inches, with all the expense of new patterns, moulds and tyre sizes. The first departure from standard was the 6ft 6in wheel on the Kings, apart from the experiment with 6ft 0in wheels on No 2925 *Saint Martin* in 1924, which ultimately led to the

4–6–0 No 4900 *Saint Martin*. This was the Saint rebuilt with 6ft coupled wheels as a prototype for the Hall class. (*A. R. Brown*)

The excellent and well-liked mixed traffic 4–6–0. No 6863 *Dolhywel Grange* at Swindon Shed

building of over 300 Halls from 1928 onwards. Later on he fitted 5ft 3in wheels to No 6116 of the 61xx class, and in 1938 rebuilt five of the old 3150 class 2–6–2 tanks, the ones with the Standard No 4 boiler, with the same size of driving wheel. These became Nos 3100–3104. Most stupidly of all in 1938 he rebuilt ten of the original 51xx dating from 1905 with 5ft 6in wheels, a reduction of only 2in on the standard 5ft 8in size. (Nos 8100–8109.)

When it is realised that about every two years or so tyres are turned down to restore the correct profile and flange depth, and are not scrapped and replaced until they are some three inches or more undersize, it shows how ridiculous it is to have new wheel sizes varying by only two or three inches.

In fairness to Collett it must be said that these antics were indulged in partly at least for the sake of a financial wangle. In the 1930s the repair fund, which came from revenue, was very short. Funds for capital renewal, largely thanks to low interest loans provided by the

Government to lessen unemployment, were plentiful. By juggling with wheel sizes and increasing steam pressure, thus providing a higher tractive effort, Collett was able to pretend that rebuilds of 30-year-old engines were 'new', and charge them to capital account. Opinions will probably differ as to whether these wangles were illegal and perhaps immoral, or just a commonsense way of getting out of a difficulty. Anyway, as we saw in the case of the 56xx 0–6–2Ts Collett was adept at getting away with things, and he succeeded every time.

The Halls were simply Churchward Saints with coupled wheels reduced from 6ft 8½in to 6ft 0in. In view of the proven excellence of the Saints in heavy pulling it might have been better to leave the design as it was and build many more Saints with just an improved cab. Subsequent tests on Halls showed a very marked falling-off in drawbar horsepower over about 50mph, and the bigger wheels would have mitigated this to some extent. If higher tractive effort was really needed, some enlargement of the cylinders might have been a better way of obtaining it.

Building more Saints, perhaps fitting some with the Standard No 7 boiler and bigger cylinders, would have been a better way of providing for the secondary expresses and stopping trains than the huge multiplication of expensive and complicated Castles. The expense both in building and maintenance of 4-cylinder engines was only justified, if at all, for the comparatively few high-speed long-distance trains making very few stops. Yet in later years one often saw Castles pottering about on four- or six-coach stopping trains, work for which cheaper and lighter 2-cylinder engines were much more suitable. The Halls were excellent and very useful general service engines, but the reduction in coupled wheel diameter can have been no help when they were used, as they quite often were, on fast passenger trains. The most notable example of this was their use on the Oxford to London expresses timed to cover the 63½ miles start to stop in the even hour, with the severe slack for Didcot East Curve after ten miles, just when the engines should have attained full speed from the start.

The Granges turned out from 1936 onwards, were really Churchward's proposed 5ft 8in 4–6–0 from his original scheme of 1901, but which he never built. They incorporated many parts from withdrawn 43xx class 2–6–0s. For fast goods traffic, and hauling pas-

Two GWR specialities combined — taper boiler and pannier tanks. No 9417 at Southall on a Paddington local passenger train, not a common working for these locomotives in the London area. This class, designed right at the end of the GWR's existence, was not typical of the many pannier tank types. (*A. R. Brown*)

senger trains over steep gradients, they had a slight edge over the Halls, and they always seemed to the writer to be a better proportioned and more handsome engine than the latter. Cecil J. Allen, writing about his observations of express train working over the very heavy gradients between Plymouth and Penzance, said that when Halls succeeded Castles there was a distinct improvement in performance, and a further improvement when Granges came on the scene. Rather surprisingly, I have several times heard locomotive inspectors describe Granges as very free-running engines.

John H. Trounson in *Steam Railway* (March 1981) has given the reason why the Granges were usually better and smoother runners than the Halls, in spite of their slightly smaller coupled wheels. They had cylinders of a new and improved design, having the centre lines of pistons and valves 2½in further apart. This was done to bring the piston rods level with axle centres instead of 2½in above, as they were in the 43xx 2–6–0s from which the engines were rebuilt, while still using the same valve gear.

I found this statement hard to believe. One had assumed that in a scheme devised to use up sound parts of withdrawn engines, the same design of cylinder would be used; in some cases perhaps the best of the existing cylinders. It would surely have been easier and much cheaper to overcome the problem of the cylinder centre-line by a slight modification of the valve-gear, rather than make new drawings, patterns and castings for a fresh design of cylinder. But under Collett there seemed to be a real terror of altering Churchward's valve-gear in any way. Mr A. C. Sterndale, who had worked in Swindon drawing office for a number of years, has checked the relevant drawings and found that Mr Trounson is quite correct.

The new design of cylinder, with valve and piston further apart, would involve considerably greater steamchest volume, making for a speedy engine. The ports would also be longer, increasing the clearance volume and lessening the compression, an aid to smooth running. There seem to have been no complaints with the Granges of the fore-and-aft movement and uneven drawbar pull that at times bedevilled the Halls and 1000 class Counties, causing discomfort to passengers in the front coaches of a train. There can be little doubt that the altered cylinder design was responsible for the Granges' popularity and high reputation, probably at the expense of a very small increase in steam consumption due to the bigger clearance volume.

Further withdrawn 2–6–0s provided wheels, motion and many other parts to build the Manors, 5ft 8in 4–6–0s with the weight cut down so that they could run over 'blue' routes. They were intended for such routes as Banbury to Cheltenham and the Cambrian main line to Aberystwyth, where axle-loading was strictly limited, but such trains as the Newcastle to Swansea, (over the Banbury to Cheltenham section) and the Cambrian Coast Express needed a powerful engine at the head. With the Manors however Collett made or permitted a bad mistake. Except for frames 15in shorter at the rear, all the weight saving of a little over five tons was achieved by reducing the size of the boiler and firebox. The same wheelbase, the same heavy combined cylinder, steam chest and saddle castings, the same heavy motion details were used as on the Granges. As a result, boiler and firebox had to be cut down very drastically. It was not surprising that they were very poor steamers, at least by GWR standards, only capable of producing a good power output for brief periods. It was only at the end of their lives that expert modifications to blastpipe and chimney by Sam Ell produced a remarkable improvement. A shorter, more compact chassis with lighter details would have saved some of the weight, and allowed a smaller reduction of heating surface and grate area. But the groove into which design had subsided was too rigid to allow anything so logical. 'The mixture as before' seemed to be the rule in the drawing office under Collet, so the Manors were virtually the standard 4–6–0 chassis with a considerably smaller boiler, a case of standardisation carried too far.

A recent inspection of No 7808 *Cookham Manor* at Didcot, where it is preserved, showed that the Manors used the Grange cylinder castings. They also had the lowered centre line, though bored out to 18in diameter instead of the 18½in. In their case though the trouble was an inadequate boiler, so they would have been unlikely to benefit in the same way. It is a great pity that although about half a dozen of the rather feeble Manors have been preserved, not one of the excellent and well-loved Granges has survived.

From 1929 onwards Collett indulged in a huge programme of scrapping and replacing the small engines which formed about half of the Great Western fleet. Churchward seems to have disapproved strongly of engines without guiding wheels, and used pony trucks on his smaller tank engines, the excellent 44xx and 45xx 2–6–2 tanks we have already mentioned. He allowed Wolverhampton to finish building a large order for small 0–6–0 saddle tanks, which was completed by 1905. Otherwise he built no 6-wheeled engines at all, except for half a dozen dock tanks, the 1361 class, and they were a re-hash of and a replacement for similar engines which had come from the Cornwall Minerals Railway. Collett at first seems to have adhered to the same principle, and built many more of the 45xx class; the last hundred from No 4575 to 5574 had taper-topped side tanks holding 1,300 gallons, in place of the flat-topped ones which only held 1,000 gallons.

For his big replacement programme however Collett turned right round, and built only 6-wheeled engines, all of them up-dated versions of Dean and Armstrong designs, as rebuilt by Churchward with Belpaire fireboxes and pannier tanks in the case of the 0–6–0 tank engines which originally had saddle tanks. This change of policy was probably justified, as these engines were considerably cheaper to build than the 2–6–2 tanks, and really more suitable for shunting and short-distance goods trains, for which most of the replacements were needed. There were already plenty of the small 2–6–2 tanks for the passenger trains on the longer branches, where brisk acceleration and fast running between stops was desired.

There were good reasons for this huge replacement programme. The ages of the scrapped engines were mostly from 40 to 60 years, and as we have seen, there was at this period far more money available for new engines than there was for repairing old ones, with the clear distinction between capital and revenue accounts which Parliament had enforced on the railway companies. Old as these basic designs were, both the 0–6–0 tanks of Dean and the 0–4–2s of George Armstrong, they were so sound that the new versions were much better for their particular jobs than most comparable engines on the other three groups.

I happened to spend two holidays in Folkestone, one in 1949 and the other just ten years later. On my first visit I used to see the heavier boat expresses with no fewer than five of the rebuilt Stirling R1 0–6–0 tanks, three in front and two behind, to get them up the 1 in 30 from Folkestone Harbour to Folkestone Junction. Five engines, ten men. By 1959, as a result of nationalisation, the Southern engines had been replaced by Great Western panniers of the 8750 series. Three of these sufficed to do the job which had required five of the Southern engines.

Churchward with his dislike of engines without guiding wheels built no 0–6–0 tender engines. Here again from 1930 onwards Collett reversed this policy, and the 2251 class resulted. These were Dean Goods below the footplating but had Standard Class 10 taper boilers, which had originally been designed for the Taff Vale A class 0–6–2T and the MSWJR 19 class tender engines. Some believe that it was the success of the latter as rebuilt with Class 10 boilers that inspired the new design. More probably they were conceived as a replacement for the older Dean Goods, which dated from the 1880s, though some of the class were not built until 1897–9. The new engines had the usual Collett side window cab to replace the unusually skimpy affair on the Deans, and most of them had screw reverse, although a few had lever reverse. With increased adhesion weight and higher boiler pressure, they were rather more powerful than the Deans, but they were not a complete replacement. Their extra weight made them 'yellow' route engines, whereas the Deans were 'uncoloured', that is unrestricted — a fair number of the latter had to be retained in service for such routes as the Severn Bridge and the Mid-Wales lines.

Many people considered that Collett clung on to office for too long. Whereas Churchward had retired at 64, Collett remained until he was 70. During the last three or four years he often seems to have been absent, leaving the routine work more and more to the assistant chief mechanical engineer, John Auld, who had been the last locomotive superintendent of the Barry Railway before the Grouping. By this time the second world war was at its worst and Hawksworth, who succeeded Collett, was getting on in years, so he too was rather set in the Swindon groove. Once again it looks as if the board might have been wiser to have passed him by, and appointed K. J. Cook, a very enterprising and energetic man, who had done great things on the production side, first as assistant works manager under Harrington, and after the latter's untimely death, as works manager.

What with the war, and the onset of nationalisation, Hawksworth had very little scope for fresh designs. His *magnum opus* should have been the Great Western's second design of Pacific, to be the prestige express engine after the second world war ended. What little is known about this project may be found in the second volume of O. S. Nock's *Stars, Castles and Kings of the GWR* where there is a very fine artist's impression of what the engine might have looked like, and the few details known are given in the text. Magnificent to look at, the engine would almost certainly have been a flop. Cylinders and motion would have been the same as on a King, with all the faults we have already considered. Smaller coupled wheels, 6ft 3in, and a boiler pressure of 280lb/sq in would have given a tractive effort of 47,000lb, and assuming the same axle weight as the King, an impossibly low factor of adhesion of about 3·2. As Pacifics are notoriously more prone to slipping than 4–6–0s (especially if the springing is uncompensated as it would have been), due to weight transfer on to the trailing wheels, this engine would surely have slipped uncontrollably. Its chances of climbing the 1 in 42 of Hemerdon Bank with a decent load, especially when the autumn leaves were falling, would have been very poor indeed. The surefootedness which was such a valuable characteristic of the 4–6–0s would have been thrown away. The obsession with being able to claim to have the 'most powerful express engine in the country' purely on a basis of tractive effort seems to have been still there.

For our purpose the importance of the design, apart from once again illustrating the conservatism over the inside valve gear, is this. The County class 4–6–0s which were Hawksworth's only major design effort, are really rather inexplicable except as 'guinea pigs' for the Pacific it was hoped to build one day. Hawksworth had modified the Hall design from No 6959 onwards by using continuous plate frames with separate cylinders bolted on, a separate smokebox saddle, and a larger three-row superheater more-or-less of Schmidt pattern. He had also used a plate-frame bogie with an independent plate spring for each wheel. The first was a big improvement on the bar-frame horrors, but the latter a retrograde step.

The Counties were basically very much the same as the modified Halls, except for an entirely new boiler with 280lb/sq in pressure, and the non-standard 6ft 3in wheels, which seem to have been a try-out for the proposed Pacific. The boiler was quite a departure from Great Western standards, with a shorter barrel and a bigger firebox than the Swindon No 1. It was in fact almost pure Stanier LMS. When the huge growth of wartime traffic began to cause serious locomotive shortages, the Stanier LMS Class 8F 2–8–0 was adopted as standard, and all four groups were ordered to build them. Swindon therefore had a set of flanging blocks for the Stanier boiler, and used them to build boilers rather larger than the No 1 yet lighter than the No 8 fitted to Castles. The latter, strengthened for the higher pressure, would have been too heavy. The County boiler was almost identical with the Stanier in dimensions, though it was domeless with a smokebox regulator, and the usual GWR safety valve arrangement. I believe that high-tensile steel plates and closer staying were used to withstand the high pressure.

There has been a tendency to dismiss the Counties as failures and a 'purposeless design', but I must confess to a special affection for them. I was fortunate enough to time the first really good run ever to be published, with No 1010 *County of Carnarvon* (spelt that way then, though later altered to *Caernarvon*) on the up Torbay Express. Leaving Exeter late, we accelerated so fast up the bank to Whiteball as to make Taunton in 34 minutes, a gain of six minutes on schedule, with 452 tons tare, 495 gross with 13 packed coaches. From the end of the Westbury cut-off up to Savernake we covered 24½ miles in just under 25 minutes, a time I had never known equalled by a Castle with a comparable load up to that time. We were stopped by signals at Reading West Junction because we were five minutes early, having left Exeter 13 minutes late, and covered 105 miles from Taunton in 106 minutes. This run was published in *The Railway Magazine* for July–August 1948, and among a table of twelve especially good runs in W. A. Tuplin's *Great Western Steam*. The run was made on 3 January 1948, three days after nationalisation.

When first built, half the Counties were stationed at London and Bristol and used turn about with Castles on the racing ground between those cities, presumably because many Castles were in a run-down state after the war. For this the Counties were unsuitable; in sustained fast running the cylinders were inclined to beat the boiler, especially as the tube arrangement on the first ten was not satisfactory and had to be altered. It is perhaps significant that No 1010 with which I had such a good run was the first to be built new with the improved tube proportions. The rather bad name which these engines acquired at first was mainly due to their use as substitutes for Castles on London–Bristol services.

On the hilly routes in the west for which they were presumably intended they were unbeatable, for example in Cornwall, between Newport and Shrewsbury, and between Wolverhampton and Chester. The finest runs over the latter route which have been published were all by Counties. Over undulating routes the boiler could be mortgaged to run very hard up the banks, and the pressure recovered on the subsequent descents. With 280lb/sq in presure to start with, there was a lot to mortgage; you could drop 80lb/sq in and still have 200 in hand!

The only other new designs produced under Hawksworth were two types of 0–6–0 pannier tanks, both fitted with the No 10 taper boiler as used on the 2251 class tender 0–6–0s. Both were a mistake — in fact K. J. Cook in his book *Swindon Steam* describes the introduction of the 94xx class as 'rather a tragedy'. Below the footplating they were the Dean 1813 class of 1882 once again, almost the same as the modernised Collet version, the 57xx and 8750 classes. Lengthened frames and a bigger boiler made the 94xx about 8 tons heavier than their predecessors, with the same tractive effort, so that their use had to be rather restricted. They were far more costly to build and sometimes to repair than the former. To suit the bigger firebox the cab was wider, and this made shunting difficult, as the driver could not reach the brake handle when leaning out. Very soon a duplicate brake handle had to be added nearer the cab side, and connected with the brake valve by a link. Having driven these engines and the 8750 class on many occasions, I can testify that this remote control for the brake was far from ideal; you lost much of the 'feel'. Two advantages I did find, however. The 57xx had a most curious springing arrangement for the rear axle which they shared with their tender equivalents, the Dean Goods. Instead of under-hung plate springs as used on the leading and driving axles, there was a pair of coiled springs above each axlebox, actually in the cab. They were rather in the way, and were too lively. They gave the engines a curious galloping motion at anything more than 25 or 30mph. The 94xx had a much better arrangement, with ordinary underhung plate springs throughout. They were much steadier and more comfortable to ride on. The only other advantage was that the increased weight allowed more brake power, so that they were better at controlling loose-coupled goods trains.

This according to K. J. Cook was another example of interference by the general manager, by this time Sir James Milne. When Hawksworth sought authority to build more of the 8750s, Milne, who had started as a pupil in the locomotive works, is reported to have said 'In this year of grace you cannot build a locomotive with a steam dome'. The LNER J72 Class originally designed by Wilson Worsdell for the North Eastern Railway around 1900, was built right up to 1951, and they were very good looking as well as effective little engines. One, now named *Joem*, has been preserved and still runs. This again shows the parochial attitude which had often bedevilled the GWR, for other people were still building engines with domes. It must be admitted that the 94xx were handsome engines (whereas the ordinary pannier tanks can at best be described as 'homely') but the considerable extra cost and the sacrifice of route availability were a heavy price to pay for better looks.

Hawksworth's third and last design was the 1500 class, quite unlike anything else ever built by the Great Western, except for the Standard No 10 boiler, tanks, cab and bunker, all much the same as on the 94xx. In fact they were not built by the Great Western at all but by the Western Region, for they did not appear until 1949, nearly two years after nationalisation. They never carried Great Western livery, but came out in black with the 'uncomfortable lion', to give the first British Railways emblem one of its more polite titles. It is difficult to see the object of designing and building these engines. There were only ten, and they had very short lives. They were even heavier than the 94xx, at 58 tons, and this weight was concentrated on a very short wheelbase of only 12ft 10in, with long overhangs at both ends. With the short wheelbase and overhanging outside cylinders they were unsteady at any speed, so could only be used for shunting, and then only over lines able to take their concentrated weight.

By this time diesel shunters were coming in fast, and it seemed rather pointless to introduce a new design, with all the expense of new drawings, patterns etc, so late in the day, especially as there were so many hundreds of 0–6–0 tanks already in service. Perhaps they were an attempt at a rearguard action, to keep the diesel shunters at bay by providing a steam engine with as high availability as possible. They were specially designed for day-to-day maintenance without the need for a pit. To this end they had outside Walschaert valve gear, and no running plates over the wheels. Apart from the French Compounds and the railmotors they were the only Swindon engines (one cannot really call them GWR), ever to have the valve gear outside. They were hardly a glorious finish to the long and honourable history of Swindon design.

Further Reading

Other books by David & Charles

Booker, Frank. *Great Western Railway: A New History* (1979)
Whitehouse, P.B., and Thomas, David St John. *The Great Western Railway: 150 Glorious Years* (1984)
GWR Engines, Names and Numbers (1971)
Nock, O. S. *GWR Stars, Castles and Kings (Comb. Vol)* (1980)
Hollingsworth, J. B. *Great Western Adventure* (1981)
Thomas, David St John. *The Great Way West* (1975)
Somerville, Christopher. *Walking West Country Railways* (1979)

Index